AN ANCIENT INDIAN SYSTEM OF RASAYANA : SUVARNATANTRA A TREATISE ON ALCHEMY

AN ANCIENT INDIAN SYSTEM OF RASAYANA

Suvarnatantra

A Treatise on Alchemy

Editors
CHITTABRATA PALIT
NUPUR DASGUPTA

KALPAZ

An Ancient Indian System of Rasayana :
Suvarnatantra A Treatise on Alchemy

Rs. 540

ISBN: 978-81-7835-692-1

Published in 2009 in India by
Kalpaz Publications
C-30, Satyawati Nagar,
Delhi-110052
E-mail: kalpaz@hotmail.com
Phone : 9212729499

Lasser Type Setting by: Quick Media, Delhi
Printed at : G. Print Process, Delhi

CONTENTS

PREFACE

This was the topic of research for the UGC Major Project granted to us in January 2005. By summer 2005 the work began in real earnest and full steam. Ms. Sutapa Saha, M.A M.Phil in History, Jadarpur University, joined as the project fellow and Professor Bijoya Goswami of the Sanskrit Department of Jadavpur University, Professor Brahmananda Gupta of the Asiatic Society, Kolkata and Dr. Jagatpati Sarkar, Superintendent, Indology Section of the Asiatic Society worked as advisors of the project.

Two copies of various dates of the manuscript 'Suvarnatantra' were located in the library of the Asiatic Society, one appears to be original and the other is the copy. We used the original work for transcription, translation and interpretation. It was a time-consuming affair as the technical Sanskrit of the text interspersed with vernacular terms were difficult to decipher and decode.

Apart from our efforts, the opinions of the experts were duly taken note of. The convergent text and interpretation have been embodied in the book. A detailed history of Rasayana of ancient times till the 16th century, the approximate date of the manuscript, has been provided by Nupur Dasgupta in the book. This is followed by the original sanskrit text, transcription and translation of the same. This is followed by interpretations by the two coordinators and the project fellow. At the end of the book, an article on the colonial period on the revival and survival of ayurveda by the principal investigator has been appended to determine the fate of such old manuscripts in the colonial period.

It is hoped that the resurrection of this manuscript, and its casting in the present state of knowledge will inspire other scholars to probe the nook and corner of this manuscript and similar ones. It may help discovery of new principles of alchemy, medicine and metallurgy. We have to thank the UGC profusely for funding the project for three years and Jadavpur University for housing it. Our special thanks go to the authorities of the Asiatic society, Kolkata, for allowing us to have access to the unpublished manuscript of Suvarnatantra in their collection and also for providing support for data collection and publication of the photocopy of the ms in original.

Editors : **Chittabrata Palit**
Nupur Dasgupta
Department of History, Jadavpur University

1

RASA, RASAYANA, RASATANTRA: EXPLORING CONCEPTS AND PRACTICES

Nupur Dasgupta

Introduction

"Athāto dirghanjīvitīyamadhyāyam Vyākhyāsyamaḥ?,

iti ha smāha bhagavānātreyaḥ?" (Caraka Saṁhitā,, Sūtrasthānam, Ch I, 1 - 2)

Let the discourse on longevity begin:

Formally speaking, the rudiments of a separate discipline of Rasāyana appeared on the early Indian intellectual scene around the 7th – 8th centuries, when the great Buddhist exponent Nāgārjuna rendered the knowledge into a śāstra or theoretical form. However, the period between the 2nd Century B.C. and 2nd century A.D. actually first witnessed the notifications about a burgeoning body of related knowledge which appear to be unconnected on the surface but had deeper links with each other. We have Patañjali (Śāṅkhya tradition) Yogasūtra with Vyāsa Bhāṣya – presenting an enlightened concept of matter or 'bhuta'; Caraka Saṁhitā compilation which exhibit a deep knowledge of the rasa as essence of botanical and zoological ingredients and Rasāyana – process of drugs preparations and treatment from these essences; and last but most important, the Kauṭilya Arthaśāstra which discusses intricate matters of mining, mineral identification and identification of mineral deposits. In fact both B.N. Seal and Acharya P.C. Roy had drawn the philosophical foundations of the Caraka and Suśruta to the contemporary theories generated within the auspices of the Schools of Indian Philosphy. According to Seal the prevailing schools of medicine and surgery were based on Śāṅkhya teaching with a methodology derived from the Nyāya – Vaiśesika doctrine with the aid of which they had founded an elaborate theory of inorganic and organic compounds.[(1)]

Around the 6th century A.D. the knowledge of materials was getting compiled in various disciplines for different purposes, viz., in the Suśruta Saṁhitā for human health, in some of the specific chapters of the Bṛhatsaṁhitā and Amarakoṣa for a lexicon - informative purposes. This influx of ideas, practices, transformed into a body of knowledge, emerged as a new discipline in the 8th - 9th centuries A.D., the most scientific aspect of which is contained in its observation of materials: dravya and dravya rasa.

Interestingly and significantly, according to Acharaya P.C. Ray - himself steeped in the history and epistemology of Indian Rasāyana[(2)], Nāgārjuna, the Buddhist scholar who composed the "Mādhyamika Sūtravṛtti", was probably not the metallurgist who composed the "Lohāśāstra", or the pathfinder in Rasāyana who composed the "Rasaratnakāra". This Nāgārjuna of the second century B.C.. times was an all - rounder - a reputed Buddhist scholar and an exponent of rasāyana.[(3)] However there is the matter of dating the compositions here, which makes it a debatable point whether the Rasaratnākara in that case should not be dated to the 2nd century A.D. and whether that is at all possible. However, according to Roy himself the Rasaratnakara was composed sometime before the 8th century A.D. He also points out that Nāgārjuna was a "comprehensive name of the activity of Mahayānism in the first phase of its onward course."[(4)]. Hence it is implied that tradition would assign all such related knowledge to the name of Nāgārjuna. Roy also refers to Buddhist tradition transcending to Buddhist Tantra genre by the fifth-sixth centuries A.D. and that the chemical knowledge got transmitted to the Buddhist Tantra genre by the 6th to 8th centuries[(5)]. Thus Rasarātnakara draws legacy not from the Nāgārjuna, who was the founder or 'systematizer' of the Mādhyamika School but may have had links with the Nāgārjuna of the Sātavāhana connection, who, according to Hiuen Tsang's account , was also reputed as a revered Buddhist exponent, scholar, and an alchemist.[(6)] However, the actual text belongs to a time around the 7th – 8th centuries A.D. and probably was initiated by another great innovator cited in the Vrnda and by Cakrapaṇi and Alberuni.(7)

Thus it was not a single person or a small group of intellectuals who deserve the credit for building the new knowledge body. The rational, logical explanation for the birth of the new discipline would be that it was the result of contributions from several working disciplines through centuries. Notably, the great, interpreter of Pānini's work, the grammarian Patañjali was also a brilliant philosopher and metallurgist who composed another text on – 'Lohāśāstra'. Besides metallurgy and physical theory, the knowledge of herbs and plants with intricate observations of morphology, plant biology, properties etc., - fitting the available infrastructure of the times – had had a great contribution. Knowledge of minerals, including different varieties of clay minerals and other natural formations, their identification, sources and properties - had been building up from the days of the earliest civilization in South Asia. The practicing metallurgists, potters, physicians, cosmetologists, masons and horticulturists (vide Arthaśāstra, Bṛhatsaṁhitā and Amarakosa) had piled up a huge inventory of knowledge and information before the brilliant scholarship of Patañjali and Nāgārjuna rendered the format of a rational, theoretical and analytical framework combining concepts of matter and what we now know as 'chemistry'. In fact, it would perhaps not be wrong to claim that the rational and scientific aspects of Rasāyana were the contributions of these practising professionals.

In the early Indian Āyūrveda parlance Rasāyana was related to the special treatment for longevity. In fact the Rasāyana section in the Āyurvedic treatises represent the parallel repertoire of the medical practitioners meant for healthy contingent of patients who aspired for more health and a long life. The germ of the idea was implicit in the Atharva Veda concept of Āyūṣyāṇi -(8) and Rasāyana may be taken to be the later formulated conception from that same germ of an idea.

Most interestingly, one may note how, even as early as the days of the Atharva Veda (C. 8th century B.C.), the human yearnings for wealth and health were closely intertwined – and the desire for longevity was measured in equal weight with the imagined value of gold. (9) The tradition of Rasatantra would catch up with this notion of all – round well – being and success in the early medieval times.

However, the core concept of rasāyana was centred round the connotation of rasa and its physical as well as chemical rendition. Rasa in the Āyūrveda genre was more scientifically cognized. It was discussed in the context of the theories of Matter even in the philosophical discourses. Looking at the Āyurvedic texts the concept does appear to have got rooted in the cognizance of the body, its biological operations and the effects of therapeutics on the body.

The development of the concept of matter in the Nyāya - Vaiśeṣika and Śāṅkhya - Yôga systems (10) in the meantime did leave their influence on the physicians, practising the often baffling and unrewarding 'art of healing'. The workings of the body, especially the processes of digestion of food etc., and the breaking down of ingredients in their minutae, vipaka, required the back – up knowledge of matter, as it was conceived of in those early times. The concept of "Bhutas" elements and tanmātras or essence of potential energy, the paramānu or atoms of which has created the universe: "Pṛthiviparamānya tanmātrāvayava" evolved in the Indian philosophy for, example in the Yôgasūtra of Patañjali. These tanmātras were understood to be of five basic categories: śabdatanmātra, sparśatanmātra, rupatanmātra, rasatanmātra and gandhatanmātra.(11) These theories had had a tremendous impact on the then intellectuals. Patañjali's Yôgasūtra related the concept of matter to the concepts of body chemistry. The impression was carried in the Āyrūveda texts and the sections on Rasāyana in these texts. Vyāsabhāṣya on Yōga vartika is discussed in the Śāṅkhya system.(12) The theories of Patañjali Yogasūtra were so famous and fascinating among the intellectuals since the early historic times down to the 11th century A.D. that Alberuni, that great enthusiast of scientific knowledge, translated the Yogasūtra in the Arabic. The ideas were extremely useful to the physicians especially. Breaking the ground of concepts of matter down to the bare levels of 'tanmātra' and 'paramānu' of 'tanmātra' was what prepared the theoretical foundations for practices which had for long times been in operation in the workrooms of the metallurgists, potters, painters, physicians and others. Rasa was the working counterpart of the substratum of dravya or matter which was composed of tanmātras and paramānu of tanmātras. The ground was thus prepared for a deeper understanding of the rasa in the context of Āyūrveda too.

Concept of Rasa

Rasa was defined in a wider sense as "the essence" in early Indian philosophical context. However, its practical meaning to the practitioners of material science was more critically garnered.

Rasa is first mentioned in the Caraka Saṁhitā as the object of rasana - gustatory sense organ.[13] The concept of rasa is clarified when the definition of dravya is laid out[14] and rasa is termed as Dravya rasa. It was understood that dravyas have the properties of the pañcabhuta and the sixty three variations of rasas also originate in the pañcabhuta.[15] Its material substance was described as manifest in the form of the five elements: ap, pṛthvī, ākāśa, vāyu and Tejas - which are causative factors of the manifestation and differentiations of rasas. Caraka mentions six original rasas or tastes[16] – which were sweet, sour and saline, astringent, bitter and pungent according to Punarvasu Ātreya, the master physician. Permutations and combinations of these basic rasas were said to produce the sixty three variations of rasas as properties of food and medicinal formulae. It is mentioned that these variations of rasas occur due to the combination and differences the substance, place and time.

"*bhedaścoiṣam triṣaṣṭividhavikalpo*
dravyadeśakālaprabhāvad bhavanti tamupadekṣam[17]

Their primordial source is water. The rasas are considered in Caraka primarily in connection with gustatory sense and its effect on the palate and ultimately human health. "Eka eva rasa ityuvāca bhadrakāpya yam pañcānāmindriyārthanām anyatmam jihvāvaisayi kam bhāvamācakaṣte."

Pañcamahābhutavikāraśtvāśraya Prakṛtivikṛtivicāra deśakālavasāh, tesvāśrayesu dravyāsangakeṣu guṇā gurulaghuśītoṣṇasnigdharukṣayaḥ".[18]

The above lines clearly reveal that the ayurveda theories derive the concept of dravya from the understanding of the theory of Mahabhuta which had evolved within the genres of Indian Philosophy. The rasas are said to be products of the five mahabhutas-bhumi, udaka, agni, vāyu and antarikṣa. The substratum of rasas are dependent on natural composition, products, preparation, place and time. The properties of the rasa reside in their substratum or dravya - substance or drug - and they may be heavy, light, cold, hot, unctous, rough etc.

All dravyas or substances contain rasa and anurasa : *avyaktibhavantu rasānām Prakṛtou bhavatyanurase anurasasamanvite vā dravye".*[19]

Anurasa or secondary rasa is un - manifested in the primordial source.

The admission to a gap in the knowledge of the basic elements of rasa is met with here- as the primordial source is never explained. The kṣāra description clearly distinguished between the natural mineral - dravya and the elements contained in that dravya - rasa. The action on effects of the mineral are dravya guṇa and effects of rasa are rasaguṇa.

"Paraspara samsṛṣṭa bhūyisthatvānna cha iṣm nibṛttarguṇā pṛakrtiñām parisankhyetvam bhavati;

tasmānna samsṛṣṭānām rasānām karmopadiśanti buddhimantah.[20]

These lines clarify that the sixty three rasa are but the results of different combinations and permutations originating with the original six rasas.[21] The knowledge that the combinations could multiply into numerous effective rasas for gustatory and medicinal purposes was no doubt the outcome of long observed experiences. No doubt the essentials were realized through experience and observation of many manifestations of the actions of rasa. The above śloka actually refers to the expert's acknowledgement that "even though there are observable innumerable combinations of rasas" and a later śloka mentions sixty three types of variants of rasa[22] - "the primordial source or its natural properties and actions are not innumerable". "That is why" , the śloka explains, "the intelligent ones do not describe the action of the combined rasas." - It follows logically that explanation of rasas singly or dually would convey the entire idea.

Caraka Sūtrasthāna XXVI, 28 describes that there are two manifestations/forms of rasa - manifest and dormant. Rasa is generally that essence which is manifest in the preliminary dry and fresh stages of the substances as well as in the form of the dravya as product of the end of the gustatory process. On the other hand there is the un-manifest form or anurasa which is the subsidiary taste.

After this follows a discussion on the dravyaguṇa – or paradi, i.e., qualities or properties of substance, which were understood in binary opposites like- parātva - excellence, aparātva - non-excellence, saṁyôga - conjunction, vibhāga- disjunction, as well as singular qualities like - Yukti or rationable, Śāṅkhyā - enumeration, pṛthakatva- separateness, parimāna- measurement, saṁskāra - processing, and abhyāsa - practice. Parā adi parā etc.

The guṇas belong to the dravyas but there is also the overlapping concept that parā could also stand for properties of rasa.

"Guṇa guṇāśraya noktāstasmādrasa gunaḥ bhiṣak.

Vidyādravyaguṇān karturabhiprāyāḥ Pṛthagvidhāḥ" (23)

These brief categorical descriptions, underpinning nomenclatures, connotations and denotations of rasa vis-à-vis- substance - perceived from the health point of view - were followed by detailed discussions on how different cases or combined rasas work in the body and affect body conditions etc. Thereafter the chapter deals with dravya first as rasa is the essence of dravya.That rasa or essence of dravya is what is to be considered when prescribing medicine to a patient is made clear in a later portion of the chapter: *yah syādrasavikalpajñaḥ syāñca doṣavikalpacit*

na sa muḥyedvikārānām hetulingopaśāntiṣu. (24)

One who is conversant with the variations of rasas vis-à-vis those of dosas (diseases), does not confuse in deciding the cause, symptoms and treatment of diseases.

In the previous śloka - it is also mentioned that physicians, conversant with the variations of rasas, administer drugs in various combinations or singly as required.

Dravyāṇi dvirasādini saṁyuktanśca rasān budhāḥ

raśanekaikaśo vāpi kalpayantigadān prati. (25)

These references clarify that in the days when the Caraka practices of the Āyurvedic treatments were being conducted, rasa was understood to be the core of all substances whether manifest in the ingredients used as drugs, or in the body of human beings and also animals as body conditions and therefore obviously as the unnatural conditions of the body too – viz., doṣas.

There is one śloka in this chapter which refers to "dehadhātu"[26]

"Tamuvāca bhagavānātreyoḥ dehadhātupratyanīkabhūtāni dravyāṇi

dehadhātubhirvirodhamāpadyanteḥ parasparaguṇaviruddhāni kānicit, kānicitsaṁyogat saṁskārādparāṇi deśakālamātradibhiścāparāṇi, tathā svabhāvādparāṇi"

Lord Ātreya tells Agniveśa – the substance or dravya (and rasa in the dravya) which are contrary to dehadhātu behave with antagonism to them. This antagonism may be in terms of properties, combination, processing, place, time, dose etc. or due to the natural composition (of the substances and the dehadhātus). Here dhātu is mentioned in the sense of "property" of the body - or rather - the concept is of "chemical balance of the substances in the body" – and the whole śloka clarifies that the Caraka school physicians well understood the ubiquity of the rasas - including their common presence both in the dravya which is the drug and the body of the patient.

Most important clue to the holistic concept of rasa is to be found in the śloka which exhorts that[27] the physician, desirous of success should administer rasas singly or in combination according to the doṣa as well as the drugs, the time etc. and the exhortation that one has to understand rasa in their various combinations and conjunct qualities in order to successfully administer specific drugs to individual patients. Rasāyana, although not specifically mentioned was implied in this sense of preparing and administering drugs composed of dravyas which are composed of rasas meant for patients with different rasa combinations in their physiognomic and psychological make - up.

Suśruta being a later text carries the full impact of the knowledge of matter as it evolved in the domain of philosophy.

In fact the Suśruta widened the scope of Rasāyana further from mere sustaining or promoting decoctions to formulae preparations of linctuses and pastes for wounds, astringents, sterilizing antiseptics for surgical purposes, etc.

Suśruta Saṁhitā deals with rasa in a more organized manner and the concept is spelt out in more succinct terms: "...........Taste or rasa is said to be a water – originated principle."[28] But more than that the concept of matter in its elements as contained in the Suśruta is extremely significant. All material elements are inseparably connected with one another, and there is a sort of interdependence among them, each one contributing to the continuance of the other and jointly entering, to a more or less extent, into the composition of all material substances"[29]

Not only that, - this later compilation carries the comprehension, if limited, of the discussions on matter which had evolved in the domain of Indian schools of philosophy by that time. This is revealed in the Suśruta Sūtrasthānam section that deals with:

"*Rasa viśeṣa vijñānīa adhyāya*". This section defines rasa as a separate matter of discussion beginning with the contemporary concept of Bhuta.

Ākāśapavanadahanatoyabhūmisu
yathāŚāṅkhyamekottaraparivṛddhāḥ?
śabdasparśarūparasagandhāh? tasmādāpyorasaḥ?
parasparasaṅsargāt parasparānugrahāt
parasparānuprabeśācca sarveṣu sarveṣām
sānnidhyamasti, utkarṣārpakarṣāt tu grahaṇam.[30]

The properties of sky, air, fire, water and earth are sound, touch, colour, taste and smell, each of the preceding elements possessing properties less by one than those of the one succeeding it in order of enumeration. All material elements are inseparably connected (sansargāt) with one another, and there is a sort of interdependence (anugrahāt) among them, each one contributing to the continuance of the other and jointly entering (anuprabeśa), to a more or less extent, into the composition of all material substances.

The next verse[31] defines rasa - as flavour in the form of liquid or rasa, which becoming modified through its contact with the rest of the material elements, gets divided into six different kinds, such as sweet, acid, saline, pungent, bitter and astringent. These, in their turn, being combined with one another, give rise to sixty -three different kinds. Each of these primary tastes is identified with a combination of the elements or bhutas. The Suśruta mentions the five elements not by the common names to be found in the philosophical texts - kṣiti, ap, tej, marut, byom but as ākāśa, pavana, dahana, toya and bhūmi. Now as to matching between rasa and bhutas - sweet rasa is largely endowed with attributes which appertain to the material principles of earth and water (bhūmyāmbuguṇabāhulyānmadhuraḥ), amla is a gustatory flavour of the elements of earth and fire (bhūmayagnigunabāhulyādāmalāḥ), salt is of water and fire (tôyagniguṇabāhulyāllavaṇaḥ), pungent or kaṭu is of air and fire (vāyavagniguṇabāhulyāt kaṭukaḥ), bitter or tikta is of air and ether/ sky (vāyāvākāśaguṇabāhulyāt tiktaḥ) and astringtent or kaṣāya is the flavour arising out of the properties of earth and air (pṛhivyanilaguṇabāhulyāt kaṣāya).[32]

However, having said that, we must also realize that the formally declared Āyūrvedic theory of "Rasāyana" was restricted to the therapeutics of longevity and vitality only. It is surprising that this extremely rational and worked – out concept of ***rasa*** in the Caraka and Suśruta Samhitā did not culminate into a more detailed and scientific concept of ***Rasāyana.***

Discussions on Rasāyana in Caraka and Suśruta Samhita

It is to be noted that the idea of "Rasāyana" as laid out in the Caraka and later elaborated in the Suśruta was the foundation on which the whole genre of ***Rasaśāstra*** was built. Thus Rasāyana and Rasatantra got confined into a niche where the main focus was not on the science of rasa but on the formulae for longevity, youth and vigour.

Harbans Singh Puri writes that "The word rasāyana literally means the path that rasa takes (rasa: the primordial tissue or plasma; ayana: path)." It is also considered the science which restores youth, alleviates suffering (diseases) and bestows longevity (Suśruta)."[33]

We have already noted above that in the Āyūrveda tradition it was held that the rasa essence in substances influence the health of the essences of constituents of the body. The rasas which enhanced strength – both physical and mental as well as promoted youth, health and beauty were especially rated as the rasa for rasāyana.

We may note here, however, that the later treatise of Suśruta (composed at least before the fourth century A.D.) had widened the scope of Rasāyana treatment to go beyond the sustaining or promoting drugs to formulae preparations of linctus and pastes for wounds, astringents, sterilizing antiseptics for surgical purposes, etc.

The preparations of general drugs for all kinds of diseases, described in the Caraka and the Suśruta Samhitās, reveal deep knowledge of ingredients and their properties. However, the present discussion is deliberately kept focused specifically on the recipes contained in the Rasāyana sections.

Ingredients

Since rasa was the core of the concept of healing in Āyūrveda, the substances, whose essences formed the therapeutic rasas - singly or in various combinations - formed an important aspect of discussions in both the Caraka and Suśruta. These discussions, including the discussions on several recipes for treatments, illuminate upon the scope of knowledge that the Āyūvedic physicians had attained in the days when Caraka and Suśruṭa were being composed (from the turn of the Christian era to the early four centuries A.D.).

Material or dravya for medicinal purposes at least had been listed in the Caraka as comprising of the following three categories[(34)]

(a) animal products including honey, milk, gorasa (secretions), pitta, basa (bile), majja (marrow), blood, flesh, excreta, urine, skin, semen, bone, horn, nails, hoof, hair, bristles, goracanā (the cow drug - a bright pigment);

(b) Vegetable products: innumerable herbs, and parts of plants of various categories.

(c) Products of the earth – Pārthiva – including, gold and five common metals(silver, copper, lead, tin and iron) and their calces; nonmetal minerals like sand, sudhā (limẹ), red arsenic, gems, salt, red chalk or gairika and antimony.

Suśruta devotes a separate chapter "Dravya Saṁgrahanīyamadhyāya",[(35)] to the discussions on the ingredients for medicinal compositions, which is a bit more taxonomically oriented than the chapter in Caraka. Dravya saṁgrahanīya adhyāya contains thirty five categories. Among these categories the majority are plant derivatives, one category comprise of minerals and metals (Trapavādi gaṇa); and one comprise of various kind of chemical salts derived from natural sources (Uṣakādi gaṇa). The category of Añjanādi gaṇa also comprised ingredients derived from various plant and mineral sources. All the categories are listed below.

Vidārigandhādi group, Aragvadhādi group, Varuṇādi group, Virātarvādi group, Sālasārādi Group (Sālsā), Rodhrādi group, Arkādi group, surasādi group, Mustakādi group, Pippalādi group, Elādi group, Vacādi and Haridrādi group, Śyāmādi group, Brhatyādi group, Paṭolādi group, Uṣakādi group, Sāribādi group, Añjanādi group, Paruṣakādi group, Priyaṅgavādi group, Ambasṭhādi group, Nyāgrodhādi group, Guḍucyādi group, Utpalādi group, Mustādi group, Triphalā group, Trikaṭu group, Āmalakyādi group, Trapavādi group, Lākṣādi group, Svalpa pañcamūla group, Daśamūla group, Vallī pañcamūla group, Pañcakanṭaka group and pañcatṛṇa group.

Rasāyana

While giving an overview of the discussions on therapeutics, the Caraka Saṁhitā introduces the rasāyana section in the Sūtra Sthānam adhyāya as the foremost part of the Cikitsāsthānam[36] among the 30 chapters on different aspects of therapeutics.

Thereafter the rasāyana treatment is discussed full length in the Cikitsāsthānam section, where the first chapter is devoted to Rasāyana or promotive measures. This chapter contains four sections.

1.1 Rasāyana related to haritaki- āmalaki including recipes for Brahma rasāyana.

1.2 Rasāyana related to vital breath or Prāṇakāmīyam Rasāyanapādam.

1.3 Rasāyana related to hand - plucked fruits of Āmalaki or Karapracitīyam Rasāyanapādam"[37]

1.4 Āyūrveda Samutthanīyam Rasāyanapadam - treatments meant for the upliftment of the science of Āyūrveda.

As a whole the chapter on Rasāyana consists of a quadruplet of haritaki - āmalaki, desire for vital breath, āmalaki plucked with hand and traditional importance of rasāyana.[38] Some of the more interesting preparations are discussed in the third section of the chapter on rasāyana in the Caraka Cikitsāsthānam, which include the sections on:

"Lauhādirasāyanam"[39]

"Aindrīrasāyanam" [40]

"Triphalārasāyanamparam" [41]

"Śilājāturasāyanam" [42]

The Cikitsāsthānam section in the Suśruta Samhitā, on the other hand, contains four distinct chapters dealing specifically with rasāyana therapeutics:

Cikitsā Ch. XXVII deals on Sarvopaghāta Śamanīya Rasāyana.

Cikitsā Ch XXVIII deals on Medhāyuṣkāmīya Rasāyana.

Cikitsā ch, XXIX deals with Svabhvā Vyādhi Pratiṣedhanīyam Rasāyana.

And, Cikitsā, XXX, deals on Nivṛtta Santāpīya Rasāyana.

The review of a few of the recipes prescribed in both the Caraka and the Suśruta would reveal the rationalistic knowledge contained in the Rasāyana tradition in the early days of the Āyūrveda.

One has to understand that, in the Caraka, basically rasāyana is a term denoting the process of making medicines and invigorating the patients through application of these drugs. The actions of the drugs and reactions of the body to these drugs was what Rasāyana was all about in the philosophy of the early Āyūrveda tradition. But this rasāyana was limited to the promotive treatment for health only. Rasāyana, is clearly defined as that section of 'bheṣaja' or therapeutics which promotes strength and immunity. There was no idea of transmutation of metals into gold.

Dīrghamāyūḥ smṛtim medhāmārogyaṁ taruṇaṁ vayaḥ
Prabhāvarṇasvaroudāryāṁ dehendriyabalam param
Vāksiddhiṁ praṇatiṁkāntiṁ labhate nā rasāyanāt.

Lābhopayo hi sāstrāṇaṁ rasādināṁ rasāyanaṁ.[43]

It is important to note that the Caraka states that there were two different approaches to the rasāyana treatment: a) Kuṭiprāveśika and b) vātatāpikā viz, indoor and outdoor treatments, respectively.

The first is said to be far more effective than the last and involved strict regulations, confinement and treatment procedures.(44) In fact the descriptions and prescriptions available in the Caraka on the rasāyana treatment clearly indicate that the procedure of treatment and the behavioral pattern of the patient while undergoing treatment were as important as the drugs applied for the right result to be obtained. Just as the process of treatment was clearly delineated and had to be followed to the word so had to be the method of preparation of the drug recipes according to rules set down by the experienced and master physicians. It was not a compartmentalized application of drugs in packages that were thought to bring results. Among these rules and procedures rasāyana featured as the core working principle – the application of external rasa to the body rasa effecting changes in body conditions to meet the requirements of health.

The process of mixing ingredients and preparation of drugs by solutions, heating, powdering, mixing, liquefying the drugs - all these involved changes in physical and chemical properties of each of the original ingredients . This was one intention of the physicians to deliberate the changes in the original ingredients as well as in the body through these combinations of preparations.

As one travels time and looks at the early medieval and medieval Rasatantra recipes for immortality, vigour, youth and charm – one encounters more and more preparations based on the uses of minerals and metals along with herbs etc. As the early medieval Rasatantra genre emerges this trend becomes more noticeable and culminates in true alchemical practices, meant for transmutation of base metals and silver into gold, which began to be juxtaposed with the original Rasāyana practices for promoting health, vigour, beauty and youth. However, the inclusion of minerals and metals in Rasāyana could be discerned trickling into Āyūrveda Rasāyana way back in the Caraka Saṁhitā itself.

The four sections on rasāyana in the Caraka Samhitā(45) and their preparations which are related in some way to metals are :

1) "Karapracitīyaṁ rasāyanapādaṁ" (CS, Cikitsa, 1.3, 3.) and the sections of preparations discussed in this chapter. For example we have identified the uses of metals in the following sections of the Caraka Saṁhitā Cikitsāsthānam:

2) "Lauhādirasāyanapādaṁ" (CS, Cikisasthenam, 1.3, 15 - 23)
3) "Aindrīrasāyanaṁ" (CS, cikitsasthsnam , 1.3, 24 - 29)
4) "Triphalārasāyanampādaṁ" (Cs, Cikitasathanam, 1.3, 43 - 44)
5) "Silājāturasāyanaṁ" (Cs, Cikitasaathanam, 1.3, 62 - 65)
6) Āyūrveda Samutthāniyaṁ Rasāyanapādaṁ. (CS, Cikitsa, Ch, 1.4, especially 13 – 26.)

A few preparations may enlighten us as to the pharmaceutical activities of the āyūrveda practitioners dealing with especially the Rasāyana treatments. The following is the description of one recipe from the Karapracitīya Rasāyanapādaṁ section of Caraka, which is prescribed for the general promotion of health in a normal person an even for a pregnant woman or for a woman who had just given birth.

The description is given in the present tense as it is a translation from the actual Sanskrit content: The āmalaka which are hand plucked, de - seeded, dried and powdered should be stored and, in late winter, mixed 21 times with the juice of āmalaka fruits again. 1 adak or 8 ser (8 ser = 2 kg 550 gm) of this powder should be kept aside. A new mixture of Jibanīya Vṛṅghaṇīya Stanyajanana, bulk-promoting, galactogogue, semen producing (śukravardhana), age-sustainings (bayaḥ-sthāpana) drugs mentioned in text (600 evacuatives) as well as finely cut heartwood of sandal, or red sandal wood, aguru, dhava, tiniśa, khadira, śiṁśapa and āsana- along with abhaya or haritaka, bibhītaka, pippalī, vacā, cavya, citraka and viḍaṅga- should be mixed together. The whole concoction should be boiled in ten times of water so that only one tenth of the original volume of liquid remains (2lts, 560 ml). This mixture should be filtered well and added with the prepared powder of āmalaka. The new mixture should be heated on a cow dung fire of bamboo chips or reed stalks till the liquid evaporates and a paste remains. This un - burnt paste should be collected and spread on iron plates and left to dry. When it has dried well- it should be powdered finely with stone slabs on deer-hide and stored carefully in an iron vessel. This powder mixed with iron powder of one-fourth of its quantity and honey and ghee should be used according to the patient's power of digestion.

The above was āmalaka Brāhma - Rasāyana, which is said to relieve the user from exertion, disease, senility, fear and helped in attaining great strength, providing a life- span of one thousand years. It is also claimed to be effective in promoting intellect and sense organs.(46)

The next concoction is directly named under the section : lauhādirasāyana and naturally involved the use of metals. The prescription went for the use of paper- like pieces of (sharp) iron, (tiksṇāyayasa) four fingers long and thin as the width of a sesamum – which should be heated till they are fire-coloured. Then these are to be dipped first in a decoction of triphalā, followed by dippings in cow urine, alkali or kṣāra prepared form salt or lavaṇa, alkali of ingudi and alkali of brush palāśa wood, every time punctuated by heating the pieces in fire (curing process after each time of solution)

After these processes the pieces of blackened collyrium-like iron should be powdered. The powder should be mixed with honey and juice of āmalaka and made into a linctus or paste (leha) and stored in a ghee-uncted (smeared) pot/pitcher(of clay) which is to be kept stored in the midst of barley stores for a year. Every month the paste should be stirred once and ghee and honey should be added to it in small quantities.

After one year the powder paste should be mixed with honey and ghee and served to the patient - a little every day - according to his constitution and power of intake. After digestion of the drug suitable diet should supplement the medicine. The same śloka relates that in place of iron, gold and silver can also be made into similar medicines in the same way. This medicine is said to promote life - prolonging life and curing all diseases. Diseases, age and death does not touch a person taking this drug. A person treated with this medicine attains the strength of an elephant, strong pravā or sense organs, becomes strong intellectually, attains fame, gains qualities of a great orator, becomes powerful and develops strong memory.(47)

The next section is Aindrarasāyana. One of the preparations requires the Aindrī (Citrullus Colocynthis - a variety of mākāl), matsyākhaka (root of kāṇṭānaṭa - thorny bush?), brāḥmī leaf, vacā (bark of Aocorus Calamus), brahma suvarcalā (Cleome Gynandra or Polanisia Icosandra?) Pippalī (Long Pepper), lavaṇa, śaṅkhapuṣpī (Andropogon aciculatus in Suśruta or Canscora Decussata in lexicographical works, MW 1047) as main ingredients. All ingredients are required in the weight of three barley grams each along with gold in weight of two barley grains. In addition kāṣṭha viṣa (wood poison?) weight of one sesamum and ghee weight of eight tola (40 gms according to the English translation of P.V. Sharma) should be mixed together to make the decoction. After the medicine is digested every morning by the patient, a diet of ghee and honey mixed śāli rice or ṣaṣṭika rice should be served as supplement. It is claimed in the Caraka that the Aindrarasāyana alleviates old age and diseases, promotes memory and intellect, enhances life-span, provides nourishment, excellence and clarity of voice, complexion and strength.[48] It is also mentioned that leucoderma, leprosy, abdominal diseases, spleen enlargement, gulma (piles?), chronic fever are cured by the use of this drug. Diseases of the psychological nature or related to the brain and nerves, which leads to destruction of intellect, memory and sense, are also claimed to be cured by this recipe.

The triphālarasāyanaparā section mentions one concoction, which goes as the following :

A new iron plate should be plastered with the paste of triphalā. After twenty four hours this paste should be collected and dissolved in honey water. After the drug is digested one should take meals with plenty of fat. By observing this for a year one lives one hundred years devoid of senility and disease[49].

The section on Silājātu Rasāyana throws some significant light on the aspect of material identification and collection etc.

Here, the Caraka begins with a brief description of Silājātu which indicates that probably it was a very rare material and unknown to many of the practitioners. Therefore, the Caraka Saṁhitā, being a practical guidebook or manual for physicians, explains the nature and origin of this ingredient. It states that - "Silājātu originates from four metals - gold, silver, copper and black iron and is slightly sour (acid), astringent in taste (alkaline?) Kaṭu in Vipāka (digestion) and is moderate (neither too hot nor too cold) in vīrya. This is rasāyana in effect and if applied methodically it is aphrodisiac and alleviates diseases. Its potency enhances if it is decocted in the paste of those drugs which are meant for alleviating the diseases arising out of the imbalances of vāta, pitta and kapha." If we look for the actual identification of the ingredient popular in the Āyūrveda parlance as 'silājātu' we find the Monier Williams dictionary pointing out 'rock exudation' and bitumen.(50) Whereas Silaja is severally identified as bitumen as per its use in the Suśruta; iron as per its meaning given by lexicographers like Amarasingha (6th century A.D.), Halāyudha and Hemachandra (early medieval),; benzoin and storax according to Wilson's identification and petroleum according to the first edition of Monier Williams' dictionary itself (margin notes) which was published by the Oxford University Press, Great Britain, in 1899.(51)

By every evidence, therefore, the Caraka description is wrong which indicates a lack of proper knowledge. However, the composer – cum – physician community did use the item but never accessed the original source. The gap in knowledge is due to this factor. The significance of this situation is dealt with below.

To go on with the prescriptions for rasāyana treatment in the Caraka:

The description of the process of preparing the rasāyana drug based on silājātu follows next: The mixing (impregnation) is performed by dipping the silājātu in lukewarm decoction and then taking it out at the end of the day, repeating this process for a week. Silājātu – thus purified and mixed with powdered metals - should be taken with milk. This preparation is said to provide long and happy life, alleviate old age and diseases, stabilize the body, promote intellect and memory and excellence if taken with a milk diet. This is followed by the directions for therapeutic dosage : "The use of this Rasāyana is threefold - for 7 weeks, 3 weeks, 1 week - superior , medium, inferior, for which the dosages were 40 gms , 20 gms, 10 gms respectively.(52)

Another concoction with triphalā in the triphalārasāyana parā describes the use of triphalā along with all six metals including gold and vacā or with Viḍaṅga (Embelia Ribes) and pippalī or with lavaṇa taken with honey and ghee for a year. This concoction is claimed to provide intellect, memory and strength, promote life-span and excellence and alleviate senility and diseases.(53)

As we shall note the uses of inorganic materials from natural sources increase with•time in the medicinal tradition of India. The causative factors may be many, but the chief among them was the development of multiple activities among the artisans and other professionals which led to the discovery and uses of more and more natural substances and their derivatives. The Suśruta being a later composed treatise includes more data and more developments in the knowledge and uses of ingredients and their properties for newer purposes of treatment. One very remarkable development is noted in knowledge of salts and alkalis and preparation of alkalis or kṣāra. These were considered as part and parcel of the preparations of rasāyana and not only as ingredients by themselves. Salts and alkalis were the rasa in the ingredients. That is why these vargas have been included in the Dravya Saṅgrahaṇīya Chapter, in Suśruta Saṁhitā where the alkali and salts are listed under as distinct category : the "Usakadi gana".(54) The Lavana Varga as described elsewhere as the different varieties of salt: saindhava, sauvarcala, viḍa, pākya, romaka, sāmudraka, paktrima, yavakṣāra (nitrate of potash), uṣara prasūta and suvarcikā.(55) Alkalies have been discussed in a whole separate chapter altogether, entitled: Kṣārapāka Vidhi Adhyāya.(56) P.C. Ray had especially noted one alkaline preparation for dissolving gall or kidney stone, which was a mṛdukṣāra prepared out of yavakṣāra, sarjjikṣāra and borax in prescribed amounts.(57) Process of preparing alkaline decoctions have been described at length in the Suśruta(58).

Alkaline preparation as found in the Caraka is close to this description contained in the Suśruta - only the nature of alkalis appears have gained in clarity.

The Suśruta categorizes alkalies into two groups: Pratisāraṇīya- for external application and Pānīya - for interal intake.(59)

One very interesting concoction of mṛdu ksāra or an alkali of middling potency is that which uses the ashes of burnt limestone, burnt in the fire of ghanṭā - pārula(60) or asita- muṣka,(61) and wood mixed with faggots of dried sesamum plants along with kṣārapāka (fresh water oysters) and śaṅkhanābhi (core of shells). All three ingredients (limestone ashes, yesters and core of shells), taken in equal proportions, should be burnt and then immersed and pressed in a kuḍava measure of alkaline water. (this water is prepared from the ashes of mixed plants like - the leaves, roots, fruits of kuṭaja (Holarrhena antidysenterica or Wrightia antidysenterica),[62] palāśa,[63] aśvakarṇa,[64] paribhadraka (no match found.), vibhītaka,[65] āragvadha,[66] tilvaka,[67] arka,[68] śuṭi,[69] apāmārga (no relevant match listed), paṭala (no relevant match found.), naktamala,[70] vṛṣa,[71] kadali, citraka,[72] putika,[73] indra- vṛkṣa,[74] sphôṭa,[75] aśvamāraka,[76] saptacchada,[77] agnimantha,[78] guñjā,[79] and four species of kośātakī.[80] One part of these ashes are to be mixed with 6 parts of pure water or cow's urine. The solution is to be filtered 21 times in succession and then put in a cauldron over fire, boiled gently with gentle stirrings of the liquid. When the water appears transparent, red, slimy and irritating (to the eye) it should be filtered through a piece of clean linen. A kuḍava measure of this alkaline water should be taken out of the cauldron. The rest should be again kept boiling over fire. Notably, this water was kept aside in an iron vessel. Into this water 8 pala measures of the above-mentioned substances are to be immersed. The mixture then should be boiled by the physician continuously, accompanied by steady stirrings. The mixture should neither be too thick, nor too thin. Then the mixture should be taken from fire, poured into an iron pitcher. The mouth of this pitcher should be carefully covered. This is the preparation of mṛdu Kṣāra[81].

Of the preparations listed in the four chapters on Rasāyana in the Suśruṭa, there is sea change in the content and tone of discussion from those of the first chapter, first half of the second chapter upto the 8th verse of the suśruta, Cikitsāsthanam, Ch. XXVIII the last half of the second chapter from the 9th chapter onwards of the Suśruta Cikitā, Ch. XXVIII to the third (S, Cikitsa, Ch. XXIX) and fourth of the Cikitsa, Ch., XXX chapters. The first chapter on Sarvopaghāta Samanīya Rasāyana not only deals with cut and dried prescriptions for drugs related to Rasāyana treatment but also prescribes some of the preparations of Rasāyana drugs for curing diseases like leprosy, jaundice etc. For example the Vidanga Rasāyana is said to be effective for cases of haemarrhoids and complaints of worms.[82] Bala Kalpa recipe is said to be applicable in cases of haemarrhoids, Haematemesis, and diarrhoea.[83] Kāśmarya kalpa is said to be effective in cases of deranged pitta and vitiated blood.[84]

Thus in the Suśruta we may note a glimpse of the transcendence of the scope of rasāyana on to a wider field of therapeutics, probably with a prior widening in the scope of the comprehension of the logic and correlation of rasa and rasāyana. This rational development of the concept of common drugs - for both promotion of general health and for treatment of specific diseases - was but a natural follow up of the trends that were already emerging through the discussions on the concept of rasa and body chemistry in the Caraka and in the Suśruta. This development of the holisitic comprehension of rasa was profoundly influenced by the contemporary philosophical conceptions of matter and the divisibility of matter and the substratum of matter – Bhutas, tanmātras or subtle atoms as developed within the sanctums of the Sāṅkhya – Pātañjala school. As Surendranath Dasgupta[85] explains: according to the theory of the Śāṅkhya – Patañjala school the tanmātras of a bhuta were all the same but the combinations of tanmātras of different types of bhutas in different degrees and numbers was what was responsible for the formation of such innumerable substances and things around us in the Universe: "The system of tanmātras forming the constitution of the atom of the bhuta being unchangeable, the cause of the difference in the composition of different substances as modifications of particular bhutas must be sought in the difference in the collocation and arrangements and re – arrangements of the atoms of that particular bhuta."[86] This broad understanding of the composition of Matter led to the holistic concept of Rasa followed by the idea of Rasāyana – that the meeting, action and reaction of the ideal rasa ingredient from outside with the rasa internal to the body, if correctly applied - would lead to excellent health.

However, if Suśruta was marked by this rational approach, it was also the witness and bearer of magical and ritualistic elements into the concepts and practices of rasāyana treatment. As mentioned above, the later chapters on rasāyana in the Suśruta reveal the gradual process of linking up rituals and religious belief systems with rasāyana treatment procedures. A few examples are cited below:

Cow's milk, with gold wax and honey taken regularly a thousand times after the performance of a Homa ceremony is prescribed as the best of the Rasāyana therapeutics.[87]

A decoction of mṛṇāla (lotus stalk) mixed with honey and fried paddy and duly consecrated a hundred thousand times with oblations in fire is considered as the best of the best rasāyanas.[88] This use of the term Rasāyana as the very preparation is also remarkable and indicates that now the concept of Rasāyana had been totally interlinked with the process of treatment and not with the drug alone. And since this process had got closely interwoven with rituals and religious belief systems the whole concept of Rasāyana was on the way to being ritualized. Most significantly, the last section in the chapter XXVIII of the Cikitsāsthānam on Rasāyana which concludes the discussions, begins with the advice that where no particular mantra has been prescribed to accompany the treatment with specific recipes, the Tripadī Gāyatrī should be recited to make up for the gap in instructions:[89]

Yatra na udīritô mantrô yogeṣveteṣu sādhane
śabditā tatra sarvatra gāyatrī tripadā bhavet.

Thus it is quite obvious that all of these procedures of treatment was accompanied by chanting of incantations and rituals.

The Rasāyana tradition thus developed with its foundations on two distinct cognitive and intellectual paradigms – one – the paradigm of technical and scientific knowledge and practices carried out in the sphere of practical arts; the other - the paradigm of belief systems closely linked with human fears and aspirations related chiefly with ideas of mortality, diseases, incapability and poverty.

To get an idea of how closely the first sphere of intellection was linked up with the development of rasāyana tradition, nay the whole science of Āyūrveda, one needs only to ponder upon the questions on how and from where did the ingredients for treatment arrive and chance upon the ken of the Āyūrveda practitioner.

Given the nature and variety of ingredients so far listed above, it would not be wrong to presume that so far as dravya or materials identification and collection were concerned this was primarily the sphere of those personnel whose job it was to wander in far off places - to the peripheries and depths of mountains, forests, water bodies. We have already related the instance of śilājātu. It is clear that several other ingredients were also generally accessed by other professionals too. A number of herbs grew in remote and difficult terrains. A few of the substances mentioned here like "sudhā" or lime[90], "manaḥ śilā" or realgar[91], "gairik", which has been identified in Monier Williams Dictionary as well as by P.C. Ray as red chalk or rather red ochre[92], which was haematite, hiṅagula which is cinnabar[93], "Puṣpakāsisā" or lead/antimony[94] suvarcalā or the plant Cleome Gynandra[95] – generally identified as a plant growing in salty, marshy places, brahma suvarcala another variety or Clerodendrum Siphonantus L.[96] the wood of Palāśā or butea frondosa and khadira, or catechu were in use by the ceramic manufacturers, painters, construction workers and metal smiths in various ways.

In fact the first clear archaeological evidence for the use of bitumen[97] comes from the neolithic levels (Pre Ceramic Period I) at a site in Baluchistan – Mehrgarh, where stone bladelets were found grafted into a bar of solidified bitumen to make a composite tool like a sickle.[98] The lower walls of the Great bath at the Mature Harappan site of Mohenjodaro was coated with a layer of bitumen, the residues of which still adhere to the wall ruins. Ochre, haematite, etc, akin to 'gairika' were popular sources of pigments even for the prehistoric artistes of rock paintings.[99] These ingredients continued in use by the pottery painters in the Pre Harappan to Mature Harappan cultures and much beyond that time in the paintings on the walls of the caves at Ajanta, Bagh etc.

The evidence for the circulation of knowledge and wide use of different rare natural ingredients for different purposes is available in texts of different genres composed approximately in the same historical age. For example the use of "srotaja añjana" or "srotāñjana" has been prescribed for eye ointment in both the Suśruta and the Bower Manuscript and the Amarakoṣa.[100] The last text gives a synonym of srôtāñjana - Yamunā.[101]. This substance is described in the Monier Williams' dictionary as collyrium from antimony said to be found in the bed of the Yamuna river[102]; whereas, the Suśruta recipe for collyrium with srotāñjana describes the substance as available in the bed of the Indus river.[103] P.C. Ray notes that "it is one of the five kinds of añjana or substances used for collyriums. The word literally means produced from a river, especially from the Yamunā……"[104] and he cites Garbe's "Indische Mineralien." He also described the substance as "riparian sulphide of antimony"[105] One may note that the Amarakoṣa also mentions another term in connection with the categories of añjana –sauvira".[106] This substance has been clearly defined as antimony.[(107)] Alongside this we have the definition of añjana in the Amarakoṣa which includes the following substances when the Sanskrit names are translated in English: red ochre, galena, realgar, calx of brass (rītikusuma), rasôt[(108)] in equal quantities. All these substances were being handled by the artisans, potters, metal smiths of the times.

There is an admission to this effect in the Caraka Saṁhitā: that it is the one who does groundwork in field who really has the information and knowledge of the ingredients. The shepherds, cowherds, forest dwellers and other such people have been mentioned as the likely persons.

"Oṣadhīrnāmarūpābhyaṁ jānate ḥyajapā vaneṁ, avipāścoiva, gopāśca, ye canye vanavāsinaḥ.

Na Nāmajñānamātreṇa rūpajñānena vā punaḥ'
Oṣadhīnām parām prāptiṁ kaścidveditumarhati."

The knowledge of identification is only required for collection of ingredients.

But then, it has also been pointed out that this knowledge and information is not sufficient. One must above all know how to prepare and administer these ingredients. Deeper knowledge of the properties and methods of preparations are required to fully utilize the potentials:

Yogavittvapyarūpajñastāsāṁ tattvaciducyate,

Kiṁpunaryô vijanīyad oṣadhīḥ sarvathā bhiṣak."[(109)]

Thus it is clear that there were the two distinct divisions in the whole matter of drug preparations from dravya and incidentally we have various categories of professionals taking care of these aspects of material chemistry from both ends who were not physicians – and far from being alchemists.

That takes us to a search for the locations which were likely to yield the ingredients used for rasāyana by the Āyūrvedic physician first and later by alchemists. Some indications are available in early literature like the Arthaśāstra and the Amarakoṣa about the possible identification of mine locations. Without going into the details of these data, it is reasonable to assume that the developments in the knowledge concerning medicinal ingredients and their uses were to some extent effected by the contributions of the professionals from different fields of manual works. The link between these activities and the practice of medicine has to be established by the new generation of historians of science so that more clarity results in the understanding of the full scope of the scientific achievements of the early Indian society.

It may also perhaps be derived from this idea stated above - of the growing links between the artisan, shepherd, potter, wine maker, metallurgist and pharmacist – cum - physician communities – that the Rasatantra genre, which developed from the 9th – 10th centuries A.D. onwards, was enriched with contributions from ayūrveda practitioners and metallurgists - chemists - both. This development reflects this trend in the uses of ingredients for preparing the potions which they regarded as recipes for immortality as well as those preparations which were thought to be helpful in transmuting metals into gold.

In the early historical Āyūrveda treatises the concern was more with knowledge for treatment of human health than with gaining mythical wealth and health. Yet, the desire for eternal youth and immortality had begun to feature in the Caraka and Suśruta in a small way. Happiness vis –a vis health, is described in the first section, i.e., Sūtrasthānam, in the Caraka in the following comprehensive scope:

"Life is happy if the person is not afflicted with any somatic psychic disorder, is particularly youthful, capable with strength, courage, reputation, manliness and prowess, possessing knowledge, specific knowledge and strong sense organs and sense objects; having immense wealth and various favourable enjoyments and have achieved desired results of all actions and moves about where he likes.(110)"

The matching results were claimed by the Āyūrvedic treatises if Rasāyana treatment is pursued properly: "From promotive treatment (Rasāyanam), one attains longevity, memory, intelligence, freedom from disorders, youthful age, brilliant complexion, loud and bass voice, good working sense organs, command over speech and vocabulary, power to draw respect and bodily beauty. It is for attainment of these good results only that different varieties of rasa are used in Rasāyana treatment."(111)

The equation between health and happiness got enlarged by the days of the Rasatantras to include wealth within the scope of

Rasāyana. The modifications sought and wrought in the Rasatantra genre also encompassed certain other features, which we shall discuss below.

Rasatantra / Rasaśāstra / Rasavidyā: Elixir of Life and Desire for Wealth: "A Way to Eternal Happiness"

Rasaśāstra texts proper appear on the scene from the 8th century onwards with the pioneering work of Nāgārjuna – the Rasasratnākara.

A list of Rasatantra texts mentioned in Acharya P.C. Ray's compendium provides the following compositions(112).

Rasaratnākara - Nāgārjuna - 7th- 8th C.A.d.

Rasahṛdaya of Govinda bhāgavata — approximate by 11th century A.D.

Rasārṇava – 12th Century A.D.

Rasaratnasamuccaya - 13th- 14th Somadeva

Rasendracuḍāmaṇi 12th - 13th C

Rasaprakāśa Sudhākara of Yaśodhara - 13th C.A.D.

Rasakalpa 13th C.A.D.

Rasarajālakṣmī - late 14th C (Karnataka) of Visṇudeva (Court poet of Bukka the ruler of the Vijaynagara kingdom)

Rasanakṣatramālikā of the mid - 14th C.A.D.

Rasaratnākara of Siddha Nityanātha 1350 A.D.

Rasendracintāmaṇi - 1350 A.D.

Rasasāra of Govindācārya - 13th C.A.D.

Sārṅgadhara Saṁgraha - 14th C. 1363 A.D. (specific dating) P.C. Roy, p. cit., vol, II, lxx

Rasendrasārasaṁgraha - very popular in Bengal, (P.C. Ray, op. cit., Vol II, lxxiii.)

Rasendrakalpadrūma 14th Century AD. (Bodleian Library, Augrecht's Catelogue)

Rasapradipa -: 16th century A.D.; Rasakaumudi - 16th century A.D.; Bhāvaprakāśa of Bhāvamiśra - 16th century A.D., Arkaprakāśa - 16th century A.D.; Rasamañjarī by

Śālinātha - 16th century A.D.

Rasarañjana of Gandhakakalpa - do

Sūvarṇatantra – no date mentioned in P.C. Ray volumes. (probably 16th – 17th centuries)

Modifications took place in the concept of Rasāyana and the emergence of Rasavidyā with these modifications substantially altered the scope of the discipline, which in fact gained a new character akin to what we find in early medieval and medieval China and Arabia as alchemy.

Coming to the fountainhead of the developments of Rasatantra, the focus is found to be on the much discussed desire for longevity and wealth as the solution and way to happiness. However, this highly materialistic aspiration was sought to be accomplished through a process that was enshrouded in surrealism and highly esoteric abstractions rendered in the Tantric mode, which was the raging intellectual paradigm within the Sanskritic culture of the early medieval and medieval Indian.

This desire had, in the early medieval times, guided human emotions to the obscure channels of transmutations in Indian theories and the latter – day Rasaśāstra texts bear the imprint of that human emotion in the most typical form of half ritualistic and muddled-up proto - scientific format which has evoked esoteric and later Tāntric nuances. For example the 11th century A.D. text of Rasārṇavakalpa(113) is a text of the Rudrayamāla tantra - a division of Tantric philosophy and practices - concerned with strengthening the human body through the ingestion of elixir. We may go into a discussion of the major characteristics which evolved within the Rasavidyā/Rasaśāstra format. The prime concern for the Rasavid was Transmutation.

- As B.V. Subbarayappa explains the Rasatantra trend of trasmutation, "The early concept of transmutation had perceivably two facets: one of converting the base metals into gold of ever-lasting glitter, and the other of transforming the transient human body into one of permanence with the soul."(114) Thus it was not only longevity, vitality and beauty which were the chief concerns. The field of aspiration had widened to include the desire for quickly gained wealth through magical transformation of base metals into gold. Wherefrom did this vision or dream evolve? Was it from the workroom of the brazier or the goldsmith? In fact, the best aspects of practising chemistry were on their way to flourish quite early and the concept of 'rasa' in its various material manifestations was already being spoken of much earlier. While tracing the roots of this concept above, it has already become clear that it was not the exclusive domain of the alchemist that bred this knowledge, but that it was the multiple working fields of operations that promoted the discipline of Rasāyana, if discipline it may be deemed.

Apart from this very major change in the scope of the Rasatantra rasāyana, there were a number of other modifications which finally rendered the Rasatantra into a new tradition of alchemy distinct from the Āyūrveda Rasāyana therapeutics.

First, the Rasa tantra texts clearly distinguish the knowledge contained and pursued in this tradition as 'Rasavidyā'.[115] This assignment of a separate nomenclature signify the awareness that it was a separate discipline from Ayūrveda-Rasāyana tradition.

The next modification is noticeable in the invocation of authority to legitimize the practices. While the Āyūrveda treatises of Caraka and Suśruta referred to the venerable names of illustrious sages who, according to legends derived their expertise and knowledge from Brahmā, Prajāpati via Indra, and a few well known sages from the Vedic tradition, most of the earlier Rasatantra texts start off with references to history and legendary figures in the field of Rasavidyā. Some of the later Śaiva Siddha texts invoke Śiva and Pārvatī. In fact the conjunction of esoteric tantric religious practices and alchemy became so closely interlinked in the psyche of the medieval Rasatantra practitioners that they identified Siva with mercury- the core ingredient as per tantric alchemy. The Rasa, metals, rituals, and Śiva - Pārvatī were rendered into magical practices. This was not unique to early medieval India but had been practised in contemporary China, South East Asia and West Asia.[116]

Thirdly, the trend of invoking tradition for legitimizing the knowledge system is continued as noted since the days of the Caraka Saṁhitā but the wordings and sentiments are quite distinct from the Āyūrveda tone. The introductory verses from some of the Rasatantra texts reveal this change in ethos. The Rasaratnasamuccaya[(117)] of the 13th – 14th centuries begins with the prayer for Karuṇābhīkṣā and a declaration that this Rasatantra knowledge will impart joy and well being to the followers and then lays down the names of several famous bhiṣags of old to lay claim to a great tradition among whom we find mention of a number of Buddhist and non – Brāhmanical sages like Candrasena, Lankeśa, Nāgārjuna, Kāpālī etc. - twenty seven experts in Rasavidyā. Salutations and the vocabulary are typical of Buddhist Mahāyāna – Vajrayāna tradition. It has to be noted that the Rasaratnasamuccaya follows the tradition of the 8th century A.D. composition - Rasaratnākara of Nāgārjuna[(118)] and hence the Buddhist tone. The earlier composed Rasārṇava of the 12th century was a Śaiva text and begins with the reference to Bhairava. The 11th century A.D. composition Rasārṇavakalpa was another text of Śaiva Siddha tradition and begins with the verse:

"Rasah sarvamayô dhāturyena tuṣṭa Umāpatih![(119)]"

More illuminating perhaps is the dialogue between Nāgārjuna and the Goddess Prajñāpāramitā who is said to appear before him in a dream revealing a recipe for Rasāyana elixir.[(120)] The recipe is described below.

Nāgārjuna, having attained Siddhi in this knowledge prepares to enlighten King Śālivāhana and Ratnaghoṣa with remedies for "warding off wrinkles, grey hair and other signs of old age."[(121)] Thus divinity and Yogi traditions are linked up in the claim to intellectual authority.

The discourses on life and longevity had already attained a foothold in the tradition of Rasatantra and the contemporary psyche of the followers and these discourses were presented as a matter of fact. The results of the Rasāyana procedure are pronounced almost like advertisements – in grandiloquent terms. But the more pronounced inclination in the Rasatantra texts was towards the transmutation of metals into gold. Alberuni's scepticism was focused on these lofty claims and the aspect of magic that had characterized the medieval notions of alchemy and not on the knowledge of minerals and substances contained in the texts.

- The concept of elixir for promotion of health is derived from the Rasāyana tradition of Āyūrveda, but the composition of the elixir had undergone a sea change. The elixir in the context of Rasatantra tradition is usually described as a mixture of mercury in compound with some other mineral, metal or vegetable substances. But mercury was the essential ingredient in most cases. The Āyūrveda Rasāyana hardly dealt with mercury as an ingredient, and cinnabar or hiṅgula, its source, was marginally used in drug preparations. The elixir is then juxtaposed with recipes for transmutation of base metals into gold, often in the same śloka. There is no such trend noted in the Āyūrveda tradition of Rasāyana.
- Finally it is the attainment of the knowledge of the process of transmuting base metal into gold that supercedes the urge of decocting the elixir for longevity. There is a preponderance of ślokas related to the knowledge and practices of metallurgy, whether correct or misconceptions, in the later composed Rasatantra texts which reflect rather a leaning away from Āyūrveda tradition towards the contemporary traditions of metallurgical works conducted by the smiths, minters, smelters of ores.

History

From the available literature on Rasatantra it is quite clear that the tradition of Indian alchemy per se began with Buddhist Tantrayāna, although the tantra genre had emerged much earlier if one takes into account the evidence in Bānabhaṭṭa's Harṣacarita. The 7th century A.D. litterateur provides a comic description of a Tāntrica ascetic, apparently of Drāviḍa origin, supervising a temple dedicated to Caṇḍikā located on the road to Ujjain.(122) The description was clearly skeptical. The 11th century A.D. evidence from Alberuni is not comical in tone but skeptical in an almost similar way.(123) However, what is interesting is that while Bānabhaṭṭa's description clearly indicates that the tantra Rasāyana applications had yet to be groomed into a formal discipline and was in fact a matter of ridicule, Alberuni talks about Rasāyana on a more serious note. He included the Rasāyana tantra work of Bhānuyaśas alongside the works of Aryabhaṭa and Balabhadra. In defining

Rasāyana however, Alberuni refers to the common notions of alchemy and explains his own distrust of all alchemical traditions in general. His comments, translated by Sachau reads: "The Hindus do not pay particular attention to alchemy, but no nation is entirely free from it, and one nation has more bias for it than another, which must not be construed as proving intelligence or ignorance; for we find that many intelligent people are entirely given to alchemy, whilst ignorant people ridicule the art and its adepts." Thus Alberuni lends credence to the methods of alchemists if not to the final result expected or claimed. He also explains the rush for alchemy in terms of the aspiration for wealth among scholars, who were admittedly poor even in those times.(124) More interestingly Alberuni describes that the Hindu alchemists try to conceal their art and therefore he had not been privy to their art. However, he also pointed out that from whatever he had been able to learn about it the 'Hindu' alchemy tradition seemed to be inclined towards the mineralogical method of alchemy and used the terms like process of sublimation, calcinations, analysis and waxing of tālaka.(125) Alberuni also mentions that the greatest exponent of Rasāyana was Nāgārjuna who lived about hundred years prior to him near the temple of Somanth.(126)

Therefore it is quite evident that some time between the 7th century and the 11th the Rasatantra had evolved as a full and formal discipline.

According to Acharya P.C. Ray the Buddhist tantras had emerged around the seventh - eighth centuries A.D. The Rasaratnākara has been dated by various scholars in the 8th century A.D.(127) However, the tradition seems to have developed within the Mahāyānist Buddhism even before as Ray refers to a tantra MS from Japan which went from Central India around the sixth Century A.D. to China and from thence to Japan carried there by a Chinese monk, Kanshin, in the 8th century(128). P.C. Ray however, places the Rasaratnākara around the 7th – 8th centuries. In fact the Siddha Yoga tantra text of Vṛnda is dated by him to the 9th century(129). The 11th – 12th century texts on Rasavidyā reveal developments in terms of the uses of different apparatus or yantras for the alchemical processes.(130) The Rasarnava mentions several of them with brief descriptions in some cases. The experts in Rasavidyā are referred to as Rasasiddhas in the early medieval and medieval texts on Rasatantra.

David Gordon White cites Guiseppe Tucci's observation that the Siddhas were eminent personalities in medieval India's esoterism and that they represent the ideal link between Śaivism and Vajrayāna[(131)]. These Siddhas were mostly invoked in the later Rasatantra texts as experts. Among the Siddhas we get the names of Rasasiddhas, to begin with mostly from Buddhist and later of Śaiva – Śākta sects. Nāgārjuna, the expert alchemist and composer of the Rasaratnākara is of solid pedigree in the tradition of Indian Rasavidyā and in fact the tradition can be traced back to Rasartnākara only. Gorakṣa of Gorakṣa Saṁhitā also has an imposing medieval reputation as a Siddha virtuoso.[(132)]. They are clearly not referred as bhiṣags nor are they linked with the Āyurvedic tradition.

The presence of the Siddha Yôgīs on the scene is attested by Bānabhaṭṭa, as we have noted, but more succinctly by Alberuni in the 11th century, indicating the growth of the tradition between the 7th and the 11th centuries A.D.

As further external evidence, we may go along the way directed by Gordon White who has cited the foreign travelers' accounts for an outsider's perspective to reveal the general notions circulating around the mystifying practices and practitioners of Rasavidyā in the time of their encounters with Indian life.

Marco Polo, whose account of the 13th century clinches with this history, talks about brāhmans, who, as he described, generally lived for about 150 to 200 years and whom he called 'ciugi' or 'yogi'. He describes quite clearly : "..............I tell you that they take quicksilver and sulphur and mix them together with water and make a drink out of them; and they drink it and say it increases their life.....They do it twice on the week, and sometimes twice each month .....and without mistake those who live so long use this drink of sulphur and quicksilver."[(133)] The passage as presented in the 1845 publication of Hugh Murray's Travels of Marco Polo from Edinburgh and London, reads as the following. Talking of the Hindu sages, Marco Polo is said to comment: "There are among them an order named cuigui, who live to be as extraordinary age, even 150 or 200 years, yet can perform all the service of the monastery and idols as well as younger men. This is owing to their great abstinence in eating and drinking; for they subsist mostly on rice and milk.

They mingle also quicksilver and sulphur, making a beverage which they drink from their infancy, saying that it lengthens their lives." (134)

After Marco Polo we have the French traveler Francoise Bernier's account on India dated to the 17th century.(135) Bernier's description reveals a tone of cautious and distant awe when he talks about the Indian alchemists. These 'fakirs' - as he refers to them - according to him, knew the secret of preparing restorative medicines to improve health and digestion and not only that, had the power to display tricks extraordinaire, which left Bernier in much wonderment.

Preparations and chemistry

The secrets of these Rasāyana scholars/ cuiguis / fakirs were contained in the Rasatantra texts, a brief and casual review of which would make any reader sceptic about the purpose and outcome of studying these manuscripts for learning about the environs of science in them or about any rational concern of historical study.

However, as the keen intellect of Alberuni had led him to track, the Indian Rasavidya had developed in conjunction with some contemporary fields of expertise and knowledge which rendered at least the working procedures partly grounded on a rational approach to the subject of substances – 'dravya' and their properties. Thus, the discipline carried an intellectual legacy which Rasavidya had inherited from the Āyūrveda tradition of Rasāyana and which had evolved with inputs from a number of closely interlinked branches of vocations and knowledge systems. Acharya P.C. Ray had delved (deep) into the heart of this hidden knowledge in Rasatantra texts and quite confidently tagged the knowledge contained in these texts as alchemy - especially related to the kind of disciplinary connections that Marcellin Berthelot was trying to gauge between the medieval Arabic and European alchemial tradition and the birth of the modern science of chemistry.

(Marcellin (or Marcelin) Pierre Eugène Berthelot, French chemist and politician noted in thermochemistry for the Thomsen-Berthelot principle. In later life he turned to the study of the earlier phases of the science, which he did so much to advance that the students of chemical history are greatly indebted to him (ever) for his book on Les Origines de l'alchimie (1885) and his Introduction à l'étude de la chimie des anciens et du moyen âge (1889), as well as for publishing translations of various old Greek, Syriac and Arabic treatises on alchemy and chemistry.(136)

In our observation of the Rasāyana and Rasavidyā traditions too, the most significant rational aspect of knowledge contained in the texts comprise of the information related to dravya and dravya rasa or natural substances and their essences or derivatives. In later medieval rasavidyā texts the ingredients are not explained in terms of dravya and rasa, but simply named in their specific nomenclature, indicating that the first identification process had matured and the stage of specific nomenclature had appeared. A number of dravya are mentioned in the Rasatantra texts which were not available in the repertoire of the Āyūrveda Rasāyana or other therapeutic sections.

A few instances of the type of knowledge base to be found in the Rasatantra texts are laid out below. It is important to state at the outset that any glimmer of rational information is inclined to be enshrouded in a miasma of irrational notions, ritualism and beliefs in magic and the supernatural.

Ŗasaratnākara(137) describes the appearance of the Goddess Prajñapāramitā before Nāgārjuna in a dream and gives the details of a preparation comprising of mercury (rasa, also mentioned in other texts as mahārasa, pārada, etc.) and gold amalgam (hemasama), sulphur (girigandhakaṁ), borax (ṭaṅkaṇa), etc. mixed, crushed and roasted together, which should be drunk. This elixir was claimed to develop the devotee's health so that his body would never decay. But, most significantly, this śloka also illuminates upon the contemporary belief prevailing among the alchemists of the time that minerals act with the same efficacy on the metals as on human body.(138) The text of Rasaratnākara refers to various recipes for transmuting metals into gold. However the essential truth in all these floating ideas is that the current practices of metallurgy worked out by the metal smiths in various fields of work got into the ken of the practicing alchemists, often little understood in principle, but observed in their procedural generalities, especially in the end result - the nature of which was again not comprehended in reality.

The later, medieval tāntric renditions of the knowledge of rasāyana witnessed the development of even more overwhelming religiosity and obscurantist beliefs. Hence, Rasa or mercury gets identified with Śiva and becomes the dominant ingredient in Rasaśāstra. The 11th century A. D., text of Rasānavakalpa declares that: "Mercury is to be considered as endowed with the properties of the six metals……."(139) "Mercury being treated well is endowed with the qualities of metals. It is considered to be auspicious. He who is blessed with mercury attains invincibility.(140) Mercury is believed to serve double pronged, both in gaining gold and everlasting youth and health."

So far as the transmutation of metals is concerned, one or two of the concepts may be interesting to study. Most interesting is the reference to the silver cupellation process in the text of **Rasaratnākara of Nāgārjuna** (7th – 8th centuries A.D. at the latest) where it is stated that silver alloyed with lead and fused with ashes become purified.(141) In this connection the cupel has also been described in another text composed in the 12th century – **Rasārṇava.** It is said that there were two kinds of crucibles: open (prakāśa muṣā) and covered (andha muṣā). The closed one resembles the nipple of a cow (gostanākāra sannibhā): fitted with a lid which has a raised head. But for silver this crucible is to be made up in two parts of the ashes of oliceae variety known in vernacular as môkha or pāniyavallī-schrebera swietenoides (clearly mentioned as Mokṣakākṣāra) and one part each of brick dust (iṣṭakāṁsa) and earth (mṛdbhāgā).(142) The process is meant for purifying silver tāraśuddhārthamuttamā-varavarṇini – to purify silver /tin into the best quality with the best luster.(143) A significant reference is available in the Ain i Akbari to the process of refining silver by the use of rāsi, which the translator has identified as aqua fortis - an acid base. Now it is mentioned in the Ain that rāsi is a kind of acid made of ashkar (Persian for Sijji as given in the footnote, 1, p. 25, which is explained as impure carbonate of soda) and saltpeter.(144) Now the use of plants like the schrebera for extraction of carbonate of soda along with the use of earth salts has been mentioned in the Suśruta to get a mixed kṣāra. Indeed the term ashkara is derived from the Sanskrit kṣāra. Thus the composition of some kind of solvent like the aqua fortis was in the making even in the Suśruta. However, its use for refining metals, especially silver probably came only after the 14th century and especially in the 16th century, by the evidence of the Ain.

Thus it is not necessarily gold which was the object of discussions, but numerous references in the Rasatantra texts read by the present author reveals discussions on different processes of metallurgy and chemistry. It is clear from the detailed descriptions contained in the Rasaratnākara, Rasārṇava, Rasārṇavakalpa and even Rasaratnasamuccaya that the composers had access to such knowledge. Whether this familiarity with chemical and metallurgical knowledge was first hand or obtained through close encounters with the actual smiths and pharmacists, is a matter that needs further and deeper analysis of the information contained in the text to match up the inner logic of the entire discussion contained in the texts taken singly. This method might give us an understanding about the scientific nature of each particular text, which might then be correlated to the nature of discussion in other texts - arranged in time frame to really get an idea about the general atmosphere of the Rasatantra genre in each historical phase.

The verses 25 – 30, in chapter I of the Rasaratnakara, refer to extraction of copper from varieties of pyrite: mākṣika(145) and tāpya.(146) It is furthermore stated(147) that the pyrite macerated in the juice of banana plant, Musa sapientum, and in castor oil (oil of eraṇḍa) as well as clarified butter and placed inside the bulb of arum campannlatum (or punāpuṅg or kunṭh), and roasted in crucible-undergoes perfect purification. Some work has been done recently by chemists in Cuba on Musa sapientum to isolate volatile components and the major ones were found to be heptyl acetate, isoamyl acetate, 2 – methylbutyl acetate and 2 – heptyl acetate.(148) No doubt the acetates in the banana plant would be useful for purification by fire. As Ray points out this process no doubt indicates the practice of smelting copper from pyrites.(149)

The Rasārṇava too contains a recipe involving the use of banana plant: *"Kṣaudragandharvatailābhyāṁ gomutreṇa ghṛtena ca*

Kadalikāndasāreṇa bhābitam Mākṣikaṁ mujjhuḥ
Mūṣāyāṁ muñcati dhmātaṁ sattvaṁ śulvanibhaṁ mṛdu(150)
Vimalāṁ sigrutôyena kāncikāsīsaṭaṅkaṇaiḥ and another recipe is as the following :

Vajrakandasamyuktam bhābitam kadalīrasaiḥ
Môkṣikā kṣārasaṁyuktam dhamitaṁ mūkamuṣagaṁ

Sattvaṁ candrārka saṁkaśaṁ prayacchati (patati) na saṁśayaṁ."[151]

In **Rasaratnākara** there is clear reference to extraction of zinc from calamine. Along with it a very significant reference was made to a composition of calamine (zinc) and copper which was thought to create gold but actually was brass by any logic of metallurgical practices.[152] It is interesting to note that the tradition continued to the fourteenth century too.

The **Rasaratnasamuccaya** of the 14th century gives two detailed accounts of distillation of zinc.[153] The first recipe involves mixing zinc ore with haridrā (curcuma longa or turmeric) and triphalā (chebula myrobalan), lākṣā (resins), sindhu or salt, bhūmouh, sāruṣara or the essence of alkaline earth[154] borax nuts and āmlā or acid juices. The mixture is to be smeared into a muṣā and then dried. Finally the mouth of the crucible should be closed with another inverted one and heated on fire. When the flame turns from blue to white the crucible is caught with a pair of tongs, its mouth held downwards, taking care not to break the tubular vessel. The result would be lustre of tin collected for use.

The other process required the ore to be mixed with lākṣā or resin, guḍa or treacle, haridrā, sarjja or natron or carbonated soda,[155] - laṇôiḥ - borax, pathyā or myrobalan[156] āsuri or black salt or the plant Sinapis Ramosa L[157] and white mustard,– the mixture to be boiled in milk and clarified butter solution and then made into balls.[158]

These references gain in significance as a literary evidence for zinc production in early medieval India when juxtaposed with an archaeological evidence. The practice of zinc production in India may belong to an even earlier date. P.T. Craddock, L.K. Gurjar and K.T.M Hegde, the three internationally reputed experts in archaeological sciences (chemist – metallurgists) had carried out extensive surveys and analyses at the Zawar mines in Rajasthan.[159] First reported in modern times in the mid nineteenth century by J.C. Brooke. Their surveys unearthed evidence pointing to the use of the zinc deposits, probably at mass scale, from at least the 13th century onwards. The postscript added to their article in the Journal of World Archaeology adds that the timber scaffolding at old parts of Zawar mines yielded a radiocarbon date around the first century A.D. (2120 ± 60 years before present) which makes it the earliest used zinc mine in the world context.

These continuities in tradition between the 7th century A.D. composition Rasāratnākara, the 11th - 12th century A.D, composition of Rasārṇava and the 14th century composition of Rasaratrnasamuccaya - clearly indicate the continuation of a rational, workable tradition of chemistry having been nurtured within the Rasatantra genre side by side with the esoteric trends and growing beliefs in magical procedures for attaining longevity and wealth.

So far as the use of mercury is concerned numerous workable methods have been mentioned in the Rasatantra texts.

The **Rasārṇava** text reads "Rasaka, - there are three kinds of it; namely of yellow colour, of the appearance of treacle, and of the colour of stones. What wonder is it that rasaka mixed with (certain organic matters) and roasted three times with copper converts the latter into gold?[(160)]

"mṛttikā guḍa pāṣānabhedetô rasakastṛdhā
Kim atra citraṁ rasakô rasena,
** * * bhābitaḥ*
Kramena bhutvā turagena rañjitaḥ
Karoti śulvaṁ tripuṭena kāñcanam."[161]

This clearly is a reference to orpiment and realgar mixed with copper that turns into bronze. P.C. Ray points out that the Rasaratnākara contains exactly the same ślôka. Incidentally this specific description of the different qualities of Cinnabar matches with actual finds. Cinnabar occurring in the Dong huan copper mines of China has the colour and crystalline form of treacle. Rock and mineral guide in the Columbia Encyclopaedia describes that the colour of cinnabar may vary from brick red to dark black. Most interestingly, the ancient users had had the capacity to distinguish between cinnabar and orpiment (haritāla, ālā, piñjara) and their different properties. Moreover, cinnabar (sindura, hiṅgulaka, darada) had a different nomenclature from mercury (rasa, pārada, capala). Realgar (manaḥśilā), however, was often put together with orpiment.

But the most significant is the reference made the extraction of mercury from cinnabar by distillation in the various Rasaśāstra texts.

Mercury is referred as the essence of darada or cinnabar in verse 37 of the Rasaratnakara.

The 11th century A.D. composition **Rasārṇavakalpa** provides the details of mercury extraction from cinnabar or hiṅgula:

Hiṅgula parinipīḍita dṛdhā
Kanyakoi / kallakoikādaśasaṁyutā tadā
Sukṣmavastragalitā sutālake
Miśrake bhabati niścalo rasah?."[162]

Cinnabar is to be pressed thoroughly and rubbed with the juice of kanya (aloe perfoliata L. or a plant growing in Kashmir)[163] eleven times. It is then to be filtered through fine cloth, and the filtered product is to be mixed with pure orpiment. Mercury obtained in this manner loses its fluidity.

The more important point is the connection that these descriptions reveal between pure metallurgical works and the alchemy of gold making.

Rasārṇavakalpa gives the recipe that sulphur - gandhaka mixed with the juice of niśācara (same as soma plant)[164] is to be smeared on the leaves of copper by which copper is 'killed' (māraṇa). This copper is to be mixed with silver, 1/3rd its weight over fire for amalgamation. If with this silver (silver – copper alloy) gold, ½ the weight of copper is mixed, gold of pure quality would be obtained.[165] So basically the verse is illuminating upon the alloying of 1 part copper with 1/3rd part silver and then mixing this alloy with gold which is ½ of the weight of copper in order to obtain what was being claimed as pure gold, but what was actually a gold alloy good enough for working by the minters of coin and goldsmiths.

This is a reference to an alloy of a perfect combination (75 :25 ratio in composition, .25 of which was the perfect combination with pure gold for gold coins under the Mughals) which was prepared and used for gold coins by the mints, probably even under the Delhi Sultans in the 13th – 14th centuries. The reference to minting of gold coins in the Ain – i –Akbari throws light on the processes involved[166]. Even before the composition of Ain, the process of minting during the Khalji rule had been discussed in the Dravyaprākaśa – a text written by Thakkura Pheru, the Master of Mint under Alauddin Khalji. However, the Dravyaprākaśa was not explicit about alloying gold and silver to obtain almost perfect metal for the coins. Ain therefore is more useful for reference, but the technique was practiced for long times and hence its percolation to the curious alchemists could be a high probability. Alloying metals for obtaining hard and mintable yet almost pure metallic tablets to be made into coins has also been referred to in the Arthasāstra. For silver coins for example, the prescription was to add one – fourth part of copper, and a small portion of iron, tin, lead or antimony alloyed together.(167)

The vague ideas related to gold obtained by the use of mercury probably has a link with the practices of extracting gold from the khāk or saloni - the slag left after purification process in the mints , when *simāb* (Persian for mercury) was rubbed with the slag to obtain gold.[168] Mercury is an amalgam for gold and this property of mercury gave rise to the expectations of the later – day alchemists. Most of them might not have really been conversant with the actual knowledge of metallurgy, yet, proved to be observant of the processes, and more importantly, the end results, an exaggerated idea of which percolated to the composers of the Rasatantra texts.

Finally there is a connection to be found linked to Āyurvedic drug preparation and pharmacology where alchemy took on the concept of lauhādi rasāyana and idea of dehadhātu and added it with the general belief in the value of gold. Gold got linked with the desire and idea of health and longevity.

A recipe for elixir in Rasārnavakalpa runs as following: The mercury extracted from cinnabar (process mentioned earlier) is to be mixed with the juices of leaves of haṁsagāmaṇi,(169) gajadhvaji (identified as possibly Hastiśuṇḍi or Heliotropium Indicum)(170) lajjakā - wild cotton tree, Gossiypium(171) arkanamitā(172) anāmikā(173) for a fortnight. The mixture of these ingredients is then to be treated with the juice of vallaki or Boswellia Thurifera L.(174) for 28 days. The mixture is to be dried in shade. Then the dried paste is to be pressed and dipped in the juices of plants like arka, pippala - ficus religiosa (or pippali - long pepper), and jatādhāra(175) This mercurial drug is to be rubbed in the liquid content of the aforementioned juices. The paste is to be made into small balls. The balls are to be put into thin bodied flasks and tightly closed. These flasks are to be kept on fire for 3 days and nine hours. During the whole duration of heating one should observe and concentrate upon the process and focus on the thoughts of Śiva. After heating, the paste is to be taken out and rubbed till it takes the shape of a lump. Pills are to be made out of this lump, which will be red in colour.(176)

The plants mentioned are somewhat different than those generally mentioned in the earlier Āyurvedic treatises. In some cases the nomenclature is different as in the case of Haṁsagāmanī, which perhaps actually stands for Brāhmī.

In fact, by all evidence, plants are used less and less as ingredients in the Rasatantra texts of the medieval times. Moreover, the recurrent use of mercury in the recipe for elixirs is a completely new phenomenon. This was the core practice typical of medieval alchemy noted all over China and the Arabic world too.

Thus we complete the full circle of theoretical Rasāyana beginning with magical prescriptions in the Atharvaveda with glimpses of rational cognition and ending with a much more advanced, yet jumbled up concept of technical practices mixed up with esoteric religious beliefs – opium to the soul. It should be especially noted here that while many of the processes, mentioned either in connection to transmitation of metals or making of elixirs, seem to appear, in themselves, to be rational, logical and technical, the end-result expected from these processes were completely irrational and illogical in most cases. However, in the process the concepts of Rasa had metamorphosed into a single item: mercury. While the alchemical concepts in the Rasatantra directed the perusal of substances, their properties and uses towards the surrealist path, the rational ideas about dravya and dhātu, obtained through the practical arts of metallurgy, pharmacy, cosmetology, cooking and distillation of wine etc., had found place in a separate genre of literature in the late medieval period. There was the appearance of innumerable texts devoted to the discussions on dravya and food, generally given the title Dravya Prakāśa, Dravya Saṁgraha, etc. This body of literature emerged as a corollary to Āyūrvedic knowledge.

Metallurgy and knowledge of gems and minerals often found a small niche among Dravya literature, however, no text was composed which was exclusively devoted to the science of either chemistry or metallurgy. Thus the Rasatantras took the stage in their absence. The actual tradition of Āyūrveda took its own separate path as did the work of the metallurgists, but never did the disciplines meet to develop into a coordinated science. The chance that had emerged at the juncture of the early historical and early medieval phases (4th Century A.D. – 8th Century A.D.) had been lost and later Rasatantra texts suffered more and more from lack of real comprehension and knowledge of the substances, their properties and uses. Yet, they are the only literary sources for delving into the history of chemistry in Pre colonial India - as was recognized by that great stalwart, Acharya P.C. Ray. We are trying to tread the path set by him in our humble way.

References

1. Brajendranath Seal, *The Positive Science of the Ancient Hindus,* Delhi, 1991 reprint, 56.
2. Acharya P.C. Ray, 'Chemical knowledge of the Hindus, *isis,* Vol. 2, No. 2 (Sep., 1919), pp. 322-325; *A. History of Hindu Chemistry,* with a word by Syamal Chakrabarti, Kolkata, Centenary Volume, 2002.
3. P. C. Ray op. cit., 2002, vol II, xxiii –xxv.
4. Ibid, xxxv. xxxviii.
5. Ibid, xxix - xxxi, xli – xlii.
6. Ibid, vol. I, xciii, xciv ; Samuel Beal, *Buddhist Records of the Westem World,* vol. II, 212, 216.
7. P.C. Ray, op. cit., &, vol. II, xli; The *Cikitsasaṁgraha* by *Cakrapāṇidatta* mentions Nagarjuna as the author of Lhāsāstra.
8. Ibid, 130.
9. Arthur Bloomfield, *Atharva Veda,* SBE, volume Introduction, XLVI, 62 – 65; P.C. Ray, *A History of Hindu Chemistry*, Centenary edition, 2002, Vol. I, IX.
10. S. N. Dasgupta, *Natural Science of the Ancient Hindus,* ed. Debiprasad Chattopadhyay, New Felhi, Reprint, 1987, 1-49.
11. Patañjali, *yogavartikā,* Vyāsabhāṣya, Sūtra 14. Pāda, IV.
12. P.C. Ray, op. cit., 2002, 59-99, 100-106.
13. Caraka, Samhita Sutrasthanam. Ch. I, 64-66. Note: Caraka translations followed for the present work: 1) Bengali version – Kabiraj Brajendra Chandra Nag. Kolkata 2nd reprint, 1996, Eng trans, P.V. Sharma, ed & Text with Erg. trans., Varanāsi, 7th, Edition, 2001.
14. Caraka, Sutrathanam ch. XXVI, 11,12,13,14. henceforth CS. and SS respectively.

Note : No diacritical mark has been put on the Sanskrit words in the Reference.

15. CS, SS, XXVI, 14, 15-22.
16. Ibid, XXVI, 9.
17. Ibid, XXVI, 13-14.
18. Ibid, XXVI, 9.
19. Ibid.
20. Ibid.
21. The Jaina Sayavada theory and concept in essence founded on the principle of logarithms may have been linked with these developments in the theory of Ayurveda treatment.
22. CS, SS, XXVI, 14.
23. Ibid, 36.
24. Ibid, XXVI, 27.
25. Ibid, XXVI, 26.
26. Ibid, XXVI, 81.
27. Ibid; XXVI, 25-27.
28. Susruta Samhita (hereafter Susruta), Sutrasthanam, Ch XLII, 3.
29. Ibid, XLII, 2.
30. Ibid, XLII, 1.
31. Ibid, XLII, 2.
32. Ibid, XLII, 3.
33. Harbans Singh Puri, *Rasayana: Aurvedic Herbs for Longevity and Rejuvenation,* in General Series on Traditional Herbal Medicines for Modern Times, Gen. ed., Dr Roland Hardman, CRC Press, Taylor and Francis, London, New York, 2002, vol 2, viii.
34. CS, SS, Adhyaya, I 67-73.
35. Susruta, Sutrastanam, Ch, XXXVIII.
36. CS,SS, Ch, XXX, 56-60.
37. Ibid, Cikitsasthanam, Ch. 1,3.3.
38. Ibid, Ch-I
39. Ibid, 1.3 15.23.
40. Ibid, 1.3. 24.29.
41. Ibid, 1.3.43.44.
42. Ibid, 1.3.62.65.

43. CS, Cikitsasthanam, Ch. 1,7-8.
44. Ibid, 1.1, 16.
45. Ibid, I.1-I.4.
46. Ibid, 1.3, 3.
47. Ibid, I.3,15-23.
48. Aindri rasayana, CS, Cikitsa, 1.3, 24-29.
49. triphala rasayana CS, Cikitasthanam, I.3, 43-44.
50. Sir Monier Williams, A Sanskrit-English Dictionary, 1st pubd, Oxford University Press, 1899, New Delhi, 2002 edilion 1073.
51. This information was provided in the first edition of Monier Williams' dictionary itself (margin notes) which was published by the Oxford University Press, Great Britain, in 1899, 1073. (henceforth MW)
52. CS, Cikitsa, 1.3, 51-54.
53. Ibid, 1.3, 46-47.
54. Susruta Samhita, Sutrasthanam (Text with Eng. trans by Kaviraj Kunjalal Bhishagratna, Varanasi, 1998.)
55. Susruta, Sutrasthanam, rasa visesa vijnaniya adhyaya, XLII, 19.
56. Ibid, XI.
57. P.C. Ray op. cit., Kolkata, 2000, vol. I, 45.
58. Susruta, Sutra, Ch XI, 6 –10.
59. Ibid, Sutrasthanam, Ch XI, 1-4.
60. Ghanta Praula or Patuli is listed dictionary as Bignonia Suaveolens Schrebera Swietenoides, MW, 376.
61. Asitamuska is identified as Schrebera oncemore, MW, 120.
62. Holarrhena antidysenterica, Wrightia antidysenterica, MW 288.
63. Butea Frondosa, MW 610.
64. Vatica Robusta, MW, 115.
65. Terminalia Bellerica, MW, 978.
66. Cathartocarpus (Cassia) Fistula and its fruit; Bhava Prakasa also mentions it. MW 149.
67. Symplocos Racemosa Roxb MW, 448.
68. Calotropis Gigantean, MW 89.
69. sutiparna is also listed in dictionary as Cathartocarpus Fistula, MW 1085.

70. Pongamia Glabra, MW, 524.
71. This term is said to cover the names of various plants like Gendarussa Vulgaris, or Gendarussa Adhatoda, Boerhavia Procumbens or Variegata-mentioned also as a plant species growing in the Himavat region –MW, 1012.
72. Plumbago Zeylanica Also identified by K. Madhava Chetty et al, "Pharmaceutical Studies and Therapentic Uses of Plumbago Zeylanica L. Roots (Chitrakạ, Chitramulamụ) Ethnobotanical Leaflets 10, 2006, 294-304. MW 397.
73. Actually spelt as Puthika and identified as a species of culinary plant cited in the Susruta, MW, 641. No specific identification is made in the dictionary.
74. No match. But Indra dru, which means the same, is identified as Terminalia Arjuna or even Wrightia Antidysnterica, MW, 166.
75. Two plant species identified, viz, Semecarpus Anacardium and Gyanandropsis of the same species Anacardium, MW 1270.
76. The dictionary mentions the term as being used in the Susruta but no identification provided, MW, 115.
77. Alstonia Scholaris, MW, 1149.
78. Premna Spinosa, MW, 5.
79. Berry of Abrus Precatorius used for minute weight measurements by jewelers especially, MW, 356.
80. The plant and fruit Tricosanthes dioeca or Luffa acutangula or Luffa pentandra, MW, 314.
81. Susruta, Sutrasthanm, Ch XI, 6-9.
82. Ibid, Cikitsa, Ch XXVII.
83. Ibid, 9.
84. Ibid, 8.
85. Surendranath Dasgupta, Natural Science of the Ancient Hindus, ICPR Series in Philosophy of Natural and Social, ed, Debiprasad Chattopadhyaya, New Delhi, 1987, 64-83.
86. Ibid, 68-9.
87. Susruta, Cikitsa, Ch XXVIII, 15.
88. Ibid, 11-12.
89. Ibid, 24.

90. MW, 1225. The meaning given is white plaster or mortar. A few plants have also been listed under this word. However, looking at how sudha is listed in Caraka along with other ceramic minerals we have decided that it is lime, the ingredient used for white wash that was actually intended here.

91. MW, 783, realgar or red arsenic.

92. MW, 363 – defines it as red chalk; P.C. Ray defines gairika as red ochre and mentions two kinds: pasana gairika-hard and copper coloured and svarna gairika-colour of gold or yellow, P.C. Ray, op. cit., Kolkata, 2002, vol. I. 90.

93. MW, 1229.

94. Puspakasisa has been identified by Ray as yellowish variety of sulphate of iron, P.C. Ray, op. cit., Kolkata, 2002, vol. I, 91; MW, 669, describes the substance as green or black sulphate of iron. Its use in collyrium would suggest that the latter identification is more appropriate.

95. MW, 1233; the dictionary also lists the world suvarcaka which is identified as natron or plant alkali.

96. MW, 740.

97. MW, 1073 – silajatu is identified as rock exudation or bitumen. P.C. Ray, op. cit., Kolkata, 2002, 85.

98. D.K. Chakrabarti, *India, an Archaeological History,* New Delhi, 1999, 123.

99. K.K. Chakravatry and Robert Bednarik, *Indian Rock Art and its Global Context*, Delhi, Bhopal, 1997, 46.

100. Susruta, Cikitsasthanam, Anagata Badha Pratisedha, Ch. XXIV, 15 – 17; Amarakosa, Vasiya Varga, 272.

101. Ibid.

102. MW, p. 1274.

103. Susruta, Cikitsa ch. XXIV, 15.

104. PC. Ray, op. cit, 2002, Kolkata, Vol. I, 53-54.

105. Ibid, f.n. 2 in p. 53.

106. Amara, Vaisya varga, 272.

107. MW, 1255.

108. Rasot generally stands for pearl. However, here the use of the reference is probably derived from the term rasottama a denotation for quicksilver., MW, 870.

109. CS, SS, Ch. I, 120-122.

110. CS, SS, XXX, 24.
111. CS, Cikitsa, CH. I.I, 7 – 8.
112. P.C. Ray, p. cit., Kolkata, 2002, Vol, II, xxxvi -lxxxii.
113. *Rasarnavakalpa,* edited and translated by Mira Roy and B.V. Subarayappa, INSA, New Delhi, 1993 Reprint.
114. B.V. Subbarayappa, "Transmutation: Ancient Indian Concepts and Practices", in Kapila Vastsyayana, General ed., *Prakriti,* J. Narlikar ed, vol. IV, *Nature of Matter,* Indira Gandhi National Centre of Arts, New Delhi, 1995.
115. Vide *Rasanravakalpa,* verse 13, mentioned in Meera Roy and B. V. Ṣubbarayappa, ed. Transltd, Rasarnavakalpa, introduction, 4.
116. Connection with S.E. Asian tradition is reflected in the Matrikabheda tantram, original edition, Chintamani Bhattacharya ed., Calcutta Sanskrit Series, no. 8, Calcutta, 1933, reprint, 1958. Matrkabhedatantram and its alchemical ideas, IJHS 1968, 3 (1), pp. 42-9; Vide Lawrence Palmer Briggs, review article, "The Hinduized States of Southeast Asia: A Review", (being a review of *Histoire Ancienne des Etats Hindouises d'Extreme-Orient.* by George Coedes), in The Far Eastern Quarterly, Vol. 7, NO. 4. (Aug., 1948), pp. 376-393; F.E. Treloar, "The Use of Mercury in Metal Ritual Objects as a Symbol of Siva", Artibus Aside, Vol. 34, No. 2/3. (1972), pp. 232-240; Stanley J. O'Connor, "Metallurgy and Immortality and Candi Sukuh, Central Java", Indonesia, Vol. 39. (Apr., 1985), pp. 52-70, for reference on archaeological evidence and tradition of Saiva Tantric alchemy in South East Asia.
117. From the excerpt published in, P.C. ray, op. cit., Calcutta, 2002, vol. I, Sanskrit Texts, 20 –70.
118. P.C. Ray, op. cit., Kolkata, 2002, vol. II, Sanskrit Texts, Extracts from Rasaratnakara, 3 – 17.
119. *Rassamavakalpa,* ed. and Trans. Mira Roy and B.V. Subbarayapa, New Delhi, 1993, sloka 53.
120. Rasaratnakara, Ch III, verse. 4, excerpt in P.C. Ray, OP. cit., Kolkata, 2002, vol II, Sanskrit Texts, excerpts section (end of vol. II), 10 and tradition in ibid, vol. II, 5.
121. P.C. Ray, op. cit., 2001, vol II, Sanskrit Text extract (end of volume II), 12-13; English trans, 7.
122. Recounted in David Gardon White, *The Alchemical Body: Siddha Traditions in Medievel India,* University of Chicago Press, Chicago and London, 1996, 49, I, – this actually reflects the attitude of Banabhatta himself in the 7th century A.D., when probably the siddha tradition of alchemy had not yet gained a foothold in the intellectual scene.

123. Edward C. Sachau, *Alberuni's India,* first pubd, Ludgate Hill, 1888, reprint, New Delhi, 2002, Pt. I, Ch. 14, 141 and Ch. 17.
124. Ibid, 175 – 6.
125. Ibid, 176, Sachau had translated talaka as talc. The correct translation would be orpiment or the sulphide ore of arsenic.
126. Ibid, 177.
127. P.C. Ray, op. cit., Kolkata, 2002, vol. Ii, xli -xlii; Mira Roy and B.V. Subbarayappa, introduction, *Rasamavakalpa,* INSA, New Delhi, 1993 reprint, 2.
128. P.C. Ray, op. cit, Kolkata, 2002, vol 2, xxxv.
129. Ibid, vol. I, 58.
130. Ibid, vol. I, 64 - 68.
131. David Gordon White, op. cit., University of Chicago Press, Chicago and London, 1996, 80.
132. Ibid, 123 ff.
133. Cited in ibid, 49.
134. *Travels of Marco Polo,* Hugh Murray, 3rd ed., Edinburgh, Oliver & Boyd, Tweeddale Court, Simpkin, Marshall & Co, London, 1845, 306.
135. Francoise Bernier, *Travels in the Mogul Empire,* A.D, 1656 –1668, Asian Educational Services, New Delhi, reprint 1996, 321.
136. Marcellin Berthelot, *Collection des anciens alchimistes grecs,* 1887-1888, and *La Chimie au moyen age,* 1893. M.P Crosland, (1970-80). "Berthelot, Pierre Eugene Marcellin". *Dictionary of Scientific Biography* **2.** New York: Charles Scribner's Sons. 63-72.
137. Rasaratnakara, ch. III, 4, 30 –32. (henceforth RR).
138. Ibid.
139. *Rasanravakalpa,* 1-52, Translated & edited, Mira Roy and B.V. Subbarayappa, Introduction, Rasarnavakalpa, INSA, New Delhi, 1993 reprint, 63.
140. Ibid.
141. RR, Ch I, 13, see original Sanskrit from P.C. Ray, op. cit. Kolkata, 2002, vol. II (end of the volume), Sanskrit texts, 4.
142. P.C. Ray, op. cit., Kolkata, 2002, vol., I, 67 – 68.

143. *Rasarnava,* sloka 46, from edited Sanskrit excerpt, P.C. Ray, op. cit., 2002, vol. I (end of volume), 10.

144. *The A 'in-i Akbari,* by Abul Fazl' Eng trans, vol I, by H. Blochmann, ed by Lievenant Colonel D.C. Phillot, Asiatic Society, original publication 1873, reprint, 1993, Ain 7.

145. Maksika identified as pyrite in Monier Williams, p. 805.

146. MW. 442.

147. Maksikasodhanam, Mentioned in Rasaratnakara, Sanskrit sloka, in ch I, verse 6,. From P.C. Ray, op. cit., vol. II (end of volume) Sanskrit Texts and Maksikasattvapatanavidhih- from sloke 30, ch. I in ibid.

148. Jorge A. Pino, Ariel Ortega, Rolando Marbot, Juan Augero, "Volatile components of banana fruit (musa sapientum L.) "Indio" for Cuba", Journal of Essential Oil Research, March/April, 2003, Vol. 15, No. 2, 79-80.

149. P.C. Ray, op. cit., Kolkata, 2002, vol. II, 3, see footnote indicated by T.

150. Rasarnava, sloka 12-13, P.C. Ray, op. cit., Kolkata, 2002, vol I, Sanskrit excerpts, p. 12, Achraya Ray has cited the same description provided in the of Nagarijuna, verses 35-36.

151. Rasarnava sloka 20-21, also in footnote, in P.C. Ray, op. cit., Kolkata, 2002, vol., I, Sanskrit Texts, 112.

152. "rasakasodhanam" in RR, Ch I, sloka 3, cited in P.C. Ray, op. cit., Kolkata, 2002, vol. II (end of volume), Sanskrit texts, 4 and discussed by Ray, in vol. II, p. 2.

153. Rasaratnasamuccaya, slokas 149-166, in P.C. Ray, op. cit., Kolkata, 2002, vol. I, (end of volume), Sanskrit Texts, 29-31.

154. MW 220.

155. MW, 1184.

156. Terminalia chebula, MW 582.

157. MW, 160.

158. Rasaratnasamuccaya, adhaya II, 149-164, in P.C. Ray, op. cit., Kolkata, 2002, Century volume, I, (end of volume), 88, Sanskrit text, pp. 29-30.

159. P.T. Craddock; L.K. Gurjar; K. T. M. Hegde, "Zinc Production in Medieval India", World Archaeology, Vol. 15, No. 2, Industrial Archaeology. Oct., 1983, pp. 211-217; postscript, p. 216; also see, P.T. Cradock, "The Copper Alloys of the Medieval Islamic World-Inheritors of the Classical Tradition", World Archaeology, Vol. 11, No. 1, Early Chemical Techonology, Jun., 1997, pp, 70-71.

160. Rasarnava, adhyaya, VIII, 31-34, in P.C. Ray, op. cit., Kolkata, 2002, vol. I (end of volume) Sanskrit texts, and footnote (3), 13.

161. Ibid vol. II, edited Sanskrit sloka, p. 13.

162. *Rasarnavakalpa,* Mira Roy and B.V. Subbarayappa, Text edited and translated in English, verse 65, INSA, New Delhi, 1993 reprint.

163. MW, 249.

164. *Rasarnavakalpa,* Mira Roy and B.V. Subbarayappa, Text edited and translated in English, INSA, New Delhi, 1993 reprint, Glossary, 144, also Rasarnava, Glossary, 42.

165. Rasaranavakalpa, 80-81.

166. Abul Fazal Allami, *Ain-I-Akbari,* Complete English tradition, Asiatic Society, Kolkata, 1993 reprint, Vol. I, Ain 6, Banwari.

167. AS, BK II, 12. 24; also see discussions in B.N. Mukherjee and P.K. D Lee, *Technology of Indian Coins,* Indian Museum, Calcutta, 1988, 13, 23.

169. Ain 6, 7, 8 *Ain I Akabari,* translation A Gazetteer and Administrative Manual of Akbar's Empire and Part of History of India Abul Fazl Allami, Complete English Trans, vol. I, Asiatic Society, 1993 reprint, Kolkata.

170. Identified as Brahmi, Herpestis monniera H.B.K., in Mira Roy, B.V. Subbarayappa, ed. Trans., Rasarnavakalpa, Glossary, 162.

170. Identified as possibly Hastisundi or Heliotropium indicum,in Mira Roy, B.V. Subbarayappa, Rasarnavakalpa, Glossary, 136.

171. MW, 895; but the Latin name provided in Roy and Subbarayappa is Hibiscus vitifolius Linn., p. 153.

172. Identified as Gynandropis pentaphylla DC, in Roy and Subbarayappa, 130.

173. A kind of plant not specified anywhere or - all parts of arka, latin name Calortropis Gigantea, MW, 89.

174. MW 928.

175. Probably jatamansi or Nardostachys Jata Mansi L., MW, 409.

176. Rasarnavakalpa, sloka 67- 75, Subbarayappa and Roy Text edited and translated in English, 64-65.

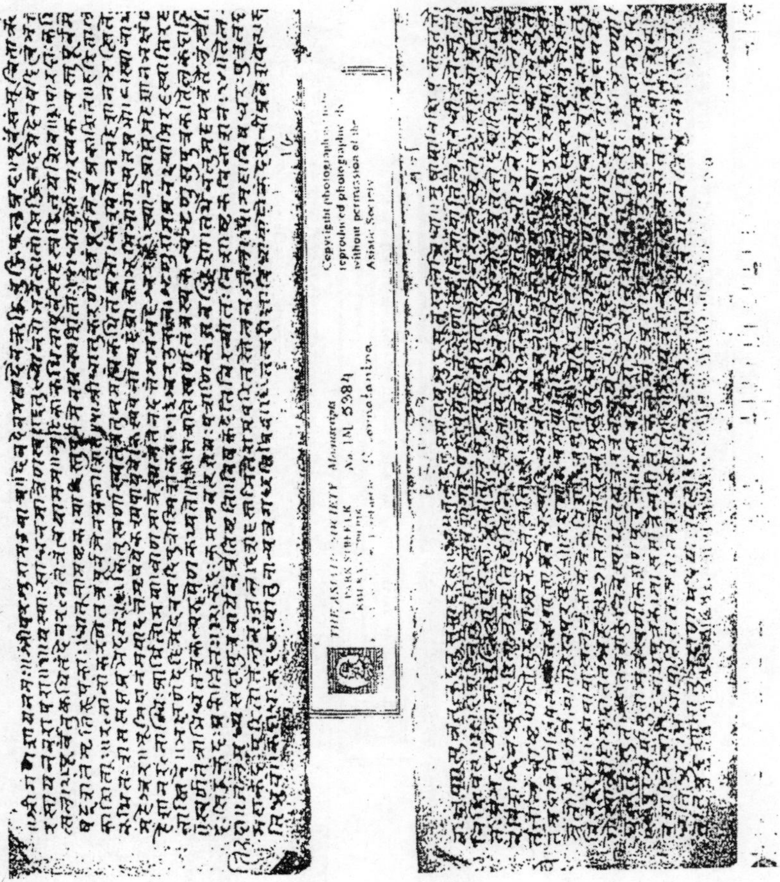

Photoplate of the manuscript IM 5384
Courtesy : Asiatic Society, Kolkata
Folio :

Photoplate of the manuscript IM 5384
Courtesy : Asiatic Society, Kolkata
Folio :

Photoplate of the manuscript IM 5384
Courtesy : Asiatic Society, Kolkata
Folio :

2

सुवर्णतन्त्र

श्री गणेशाय नमः ॥

श्री परशुराम उवाच॥

देव देव महादेव ऋद्धि बुद्धि फलप्रद।
पुवें संस्तुचिता ऋद्धि रसायनपरा वरा ॥ 1 ॥

यस्याः साधनमात्रेण स्वराट् तुल्यो नरो भवेत्।
तां सिद्धिं वद मे देव यदित्वं भक्तवत्सलः॥ 2 ॥

पुर्वं तु कथितं देव रत्न तत्रं त्वया मम।
गुढिकाः कथितं पुर्व सहस्त्रद्वितयं शिव ॥ 3 ॥

पारदाः कथिताः षट्शत मृतिरूपकाः ।
धातुनामष्टकल्पास्तु पूर्वमेव प्रकाशिताः ॥ 4 ॥

धातुर्योगारव्याकल्पास्तु पूर्वमेव प्रकाशिताः ।
रत्नानं, करणे तन्त्रं पूर्वमेव प्रकाशितं ॥ 5 ॥

श्रीधातुकरणे तन्त्रं पूर्वमेव प्रकाशितं।
हरितालस्तु कथितः शतसप्तप्रभेदतः ॥ 6 ॥

किन्तु स्वर्णाख्यातन्त्रं तु न मध्य कथितं प्रभो।
कश्यपेन महेशान, भर्त्सितोऽस्मि महेश्वर ॥ 7 ॥

भुमिदानं मया दत्रमृष्ये कश्यपाय वै।
कश्यपेनाप्यहं प्रोक्तो भुमिभागं त्यज प्रभो ॥ 8 ॥

स्मानार्था/स्थानार्थं तु महेशान रत्नाब्धिः प्रार्थितो मया ।
वाणमात्र स्थलं तेन दत्तं मम महेश्वर ॥ 9 ॥

स्थानं प्राप्ते महेशान भक्षणं मम नास्ति वै ।
भक्षणं देहि मे देव यदि पुत्रोस्मि शंकर ॥ 10 ॥

ईस्वर उवाचं।

शृणु राम प्रवक्ष्यामि रहस्याति रहस्यकं।
स्वर्णतन्त्रामिधं तत्रं कल्प रूपेन कथ्यते ।। 11 ।।

तत्रादौ स्वर्णतंत्रस्य कल्पं शृणु सुपुत्रक ।
तैलकन्दाभिध कन्दः सिद्ध कन्दः प्रकीर्त्तितः ।। 12 ।।

कन्दः कमलवतज्ञेयः पत्राणि कंज वद्विशे।
तथैव तु महपत्रं (महत्पत्रं) तैलं स्रवति सर्वदा ।। 13 ।।

जलमध्यं सदापुत्र वार्येव (इ) प्रतिष्ठति ।
विष कन्देति विख्यातः विशाषृक विनाशनः ।। 14 ।।

तैलस्रावी महाकन्दः परितोस्तैलवज्जकं ।
दशहस्तमिते राम परितस्तैलवज्जलम ।। 15 ।।

महाविषधरः पुत्र तदधो वसति ध्रुवं ।
कन्दाधः कन्दछायातु नान्यत्र गच्छति प्रिय ।। 16 ।।

तत् परीक्षा विधायादौ कन्दे सुचीं प्रवेशयेत ।
सुचीं द्रावाक्षणात् पुत्र (सुत्र) तत् कन्दं तु समाहरेत ।। 17 ।।

तत्कन्दं तु समादाय शुद्ध सुतं खलेत त्रिधा (?) ।
मुषायां निक्षिपेत्तं तु तत्तैलं तत्र निक्षिपेत ।। 18 ।।

दीपान्गि तु महाराम वशागारेण दीपयेत ।
तत्क्षणात् मृतिमायाति लक्षावेधी भवेत सुत ।। 19 ।।

ततः प्रभक्षयद्राम क्षुन्निद्राहारको ध्रुवमः।
तालं शुद्धं समानीय तत्तैलेन खलेत सुत ।। 20 ।।

सप्तधा प्रत्यहं राम तेवं विशंद्धिनं ध्रुवं ।
हरितालो मृति र्धेति निर्धुमो जायते ध्रुवं ।। 21 ।।

अन्ग्रौ पुत्र ततो दधा निर्धुमो जायते सुत ।
तत्तालं चाष्ढं धातौ तु दध्या द्रावकते/दद्धाद्रावेकृत सति ।। 22 ।।

सर्ववेधी भवेदेव शतवेधी भवेत ध्रुवं ।
तत्तैलं तु समादाय तत्र ताम्र द्रावे विनिक्षिपेत ।। 23 ।।

ततक्षणात् ताम्र वेधस्या दिब्यं भवति कांचनं ।
वंगे कांस्ये यदा दध्यातदा रोप्यं भवेत सुत ।। 24 ।।

ताम्रं लोहे तथा रीत्यां तारे खर्पर[1] सुतके ।
त(त्)क्षणा द्रौप्यमायाति दिव्यं भवति कांचनम् ॥ 25 ॥

उदरसमा[2] पारद तु समानीय (समादाय) विलक्षणः ।
छायायां खलनं कार्यमेकविशंदिनं सुत ॥ 26 ॥

लोहं यन्त्रे ततो दद्धयात् पारदस्य रससंयुत ।
उभौ समानभागौ स्थाल्लौहो मुद्रां ततश्चरेत[3] ॥ 27 ॥

ततो घोरास्य मुद्रां तु दध्यात (?) तध्यौत (?) क्रमेच, (क्रमेणच) ।
तद्यत्र चुल्लिकायां स्थापयेद (त्) यत्नेन सुत ॥ 28 ॥

तत्र शंकुनिवेश्याय (?) तधत्रं (?) तद्यन्त्रं वधयेत् ।
आदौ दीपाग्निमारभ्य ह्टाग्नि दापयेततः ॥ 29 ॥

स्व/श्री पुरश्चर्या पुतो यन्त्रं स्वर्णं आर्कषण पुर्वक ।
ब्रह्मचर्यपरोभूत्वा तत्राग्निं दापयेत, सुत ॥ 30 ॥

अरण्याग्नि तु वंशग्नि खदिरे चाथ पुत्रक ।
मास मात्रे व्यतीते तु कालमात्र प्रजायते ॥ 31 ॥

उड्डीय प्रथमं राम मुद्राया गच्छति ध्रुवं ।
अधोयाति ततः सुतः तत्र शब्दं करोति हि ॥ 32 ॥

यत्र शब्दो भवेत पुत्र क (?)[4] तत्र समादिशेत ।
क (?) तत्र प्रद शोभातुन अनुभक्षणार्थ प्रयोज्ञपेत (प्रयोजयेत) ॥ 33 ॥

सुधाकरः काम (कासं) (कारि)? (वोगरि/वगंरि)? सर्वथा भवति ध्रुवम् ।
कलांशोडंश (?) युक्तो हि शतवेधी भवेत ध्रुवम ॥ 34 ॥

एवं द्वादशमासं तमाग्नि देयो द्विजोत्तम ॥ 35 ॥
तत्कन्दछायावृक्षे तु सदा तिष्ठति पुत्रक (पुत्र) ?

इति संक्षेपतः प्रोक्तः किमन्यत् श्रुतमिच्छसिं ।
इति स्वर्णतन्त्रेशिवपरशुराम संवादे तैलकन्द कल्पः॥

राम उवाच ॥
कटु कुष्माप्डकल्पो हि सुचितं कथय प्रभो ।
शिव (उवाच)
कटु कुष्माण्डमादायतद्रसं ग्राहयेत् शुद्धोः ॥ 1 ॥

वंगे दध्यात्यदा पुत्र तदा रौप्यं प्रजायते ।
ताम्रलोहे तथा रीत्या ढंकणं तद्रसंक्षिपेत् ॥ 2 ॥

तत्क्षणात् स्वर्णतो याति स्वर्ण जाबूंनदं भवेत ।
तद्रसे तारसयुंक्रं सप्तधातुं खलेत सुत ।। 3 ।।

एवं मुनि (?) दिनं पुत्र खलित्वा तु पुनः पुनः ।
कलंकस्तु भवेत सिद्धो शतवेधी भवेत सुत ।। 4 ।।

इति स्वर्णाकल्पः (कदुकुष्माण्डकल्पः)[5]

अथान्यं संप्रवक्ष्यामि रामसावहितो भव ।
रक्तवीजकदु गृह्य ऋद्धिवल्यभिधो सुत ।। 1 ।।

ताम्र संशोध्य यत्नेन तत्ताम्र तु रसं क्षिपेत ।
तत्राम्रं स्वर्णनं याति गांगेय भवति ध्रुवम ।। 2 ।।

जलं वंस्ये कृत्वादौ रसंतत्र विनिक्षिपेत ।
तत्क्षणात् द्रौप्या तां याति कुंन्दपुष्प समप्रभां ।। 3 ।।

तद्रौप्यं तु समादाय तद्रसेन तु संखलेत् ।
दिनैकं तु खलेत पुत्रकलंको भवति ध्रुवम ।। 4 ।।

तत् कलंकं तु समारत्तिकार्द्धं द्विजोत्तम ।

धातुमात्रे विनिक्षप्य रक्कामिवेधी मिवेधी भवेत सुत ।। 5 ।।

इति स्वर्ण कल्पः (कदुरक्तवोज)
अथन्यत्सं प्रवक्ष्यामि ।

कटु तुम्वाविधं सुत ।
कटु तुंवी वने गत्वा मंत्र प्रार्थन् पुर्वकं ।। 1 ।।

वीज सार कटु देव दृष्टे तु वदनं कटुत्व ।
ईदशस्य तु कल्पो हि कार्यो यत्न'न मता ।। 2 ।।

सुचिका पीत्तलानां च वह्वः कारयेत सुत ।
कार्त्तिके समनुप्राप्ते फले सुचीं प्रवेशयेत् ।। 3 ।।

युत्त्स्या प्रवेश य कार्ये बीजवेद्यो यथा न च ।
पंच (पञ्च), चत्वारः पंञ्चशः षष्ठः सप्ताष्ठो नव वा प्रिय ।। 4 ।।
अमाधस्य समाध्य तं फलानि च अवलोकयेत ।
वीजंवधे समुतपन्ने फलं नश्यति तु ध्रुवम ।। 5 ।।

त्रिमास तत्र शयनं कार्यं यत्नेन धीमता ।
यध्यत् फलं भवेन्नष्ढं तत्रत्याज्यं ततः सुत ।। 6 ।।

तद्रसेन तु सा सुच्यः सिद्धा एव भवन्ति हि ।
मासोत्तरं परशुराम तेषां निष्कासनं चरेत ।। 7 ।।

सुचीनाम (अ)ग्नि संयोगः कार्यश्चाम्ना ययोगतः ।
वनोपलायास्तंगार[6] कृत्वा चैव शरावके ॥ 8 ॥

तत्र सुच्यस्तु निक्षिप्य स्वर्णं भ(व)ति काञ्चनं ।
शरवद्वयसंरूद्ध(ाः) सुच्यः कार्या(:) प्रयत्नतः॥ 9 ॥

कुक्कुढाख्यपुटेनैव कृत्वा चैव श(रा)वके[7] ।
भवेज्जाबुँनदप्रभं वंशांगारेण[8] वादेयं वनोपल प्रयोगतः[8] ॥ 10 ॥

अथवा मुषिकां दत्वा तत्र देयातु सुचिका ।
तत्र ध्मातो महेश इष्ट दिव्यं भवति काञ्चनम् ॥ 11 ॥

अंगारमध्ये सुचीनां स्थापनं तु समाचरेत ।
ध्मातं भवति विप्रेन्द्र दिव्यं भवति काञ्चनम् ॥ 12 ॥

इति स्वर्णतन्त्रे कटुतुम्बीक (ल्पस्य) चतुर्थः ।

अथान्यत् संप्रवक्ष्यामि सिद्धतुम्बी श्रीसुसिधिदां ।
आदौ वंगं सुषोध्याय मुषिकायां विनिक्षिपेत ॥ 1 ॥

श्वेता तु गिरिकर्णो तु योनिवल्यमिधां सुत ।
तद्रसं तत्र निक्षिप्यधमे यत्नेन पुंगव ॥ 2 ॥
तदवंग जायते शुद्धं कुद(न्द) पुष्पसमप्रभां ।
इति स्वर्ण पञ्चमः ॥

अथान्यत् प्रवक्ष्यामि श्वेतगोक्षुरक कल्पकं ।
येन विज्ञानमात्रेण रसायनवर भवेत ॥ 1 ॥

वगं संशोध्य यत्नेन तत्रगोक्षुरजरसं ।
निक्षिप्य प्रधामेत (?) पुत्र वंगस्तारुत्वतां त्यजेत् ॥ 2 ॥
इति षष्ठः ॥

अथान्यत् संप्रवक्ष्यामि श्वेतैरडंस्यकल्पकम।
श्वेतैरडस्य मूलं तु गृहीत्वा पुष्य भास्करे ॥ 1 ॥

ततैलेन सुधृष्टं तु कर्पुरेण समन्वितं ।
अञ्जनेत्रयुगलं सप्तपातालदुर्शणं ॥ 2 ॥

सिद्धाजंनमिदं सिद्धं सिद्धयोग विनिर्मितम ।
तन्मुलमार्गपाषानं शुद्धसूत समन्वितं ॥ 3 ॥

कृष्ट चद्रवसंपिष्टं शुद्धं मुषागतं धयेत ।
शलमली खदिरांगारैस्त्रिधावंगे भवत्यलम् ॥ 4 ॥

तद्वंगेषु द्रुतौ क्षिप्रं सहस्रांशो वेधकम ।
वीजं श्वेतं तथा पुष्पमध्यस्य श्वेत एवहि ॥ 5 ॥

वीजं रक्तं तथा पुष्पं फलं रक्तं प्रकीर्तितम ।
तत्कल्पः श्वेतवज्ज्ञेयः सर्वसिद्धिप्रदो वतः ॥ 6 ॥

इति सप्तमः (इति स्वर्णतन्त्रे रक्तकल्पेः सप्तमः)

काकरिकल्पं देवेश श्रृणु यत्नेन साम्प्रतम् ।
काकरिः काकं तु शब्दौ वै पर्यायवाचकौ ॥ 1 ॥

पुष्यर्कं फलं गृह्य सुपक्कम सुमनोहरम् ।
तत्फलस्य रसेनैव पारदं सुदृढ़ खलेत ॥ 2 ॥

दिनमात्रं खलेद्देव बद्धो भवति पारदः ।
एवं विंशद्दिनं देव तद्रसेन तु मेलयेत् ॥ 3 ॥

रस संमेलनात् एव गुढीषष्ठिमुखा मता ।
तस्याः सन्धारणा .... षष्ठिसिद्धेश्वरो भवेत ॥ 4 ॥

तत्पञ्चांगरसनैव पारद संखलेत् सुत ।
तं मुषिकायां निक्षिप्य तं रसं तु पुर्नददेत ॥ 5 ॥

एवं प्रहरमात्रे तु तद्रसं तत्र निक्षिपेत् ।
एवं क्रमेण सत्पुत्र पारदौ मृतिमेष्यति ॥ 6 ॥

तं पारदं तु सत्पुत्र रक्तिकादश (रत्तिकादश) संमासकं ।
भक्षयेत् यत्नतः पुत्र चिरंजीवी भवेत् सतु ॥ 7 ॥

वलिपलितनिर्मुक्तो कामरूपी भवेत स तु ।
तथैव प्रस्य[9] साहस्रसंभक्षो भवेत्येव नरः सुत ॥ 8 ॥

हरिताले तद्रसं तु दत्वा तु खलेनं चरेत ।
यामाष्ठौ संखलेत् पुत्र निर्धुमो भर्वात ध्रुवम ॥ 9 ॥

त्तिकार्धं भक्षयेतं गुणः पारदवद् भवेत ।
तं पारदं तु कनके लक्षवेधी भवेत सुत ॥ 10 ॥

तथैव तालकः पुत्र शतवेधी प्रजायते ।
तं पत्रस्य रसं पुत्र वंगमध्ये विनिक्षिपेत् ॥ 11 ॥

तत्तारं जायते शुद्धं कुन्दपुष्पसमप्रभम ।
तस्य पुष्प रसः पुत्र धातुमात्रप्रवेधकृत ॥ 12 ॥

तत्फलस्य रसं पुत्र ताम्र द्रावे विनिक्षिपेत ।
सुवर्ण जायते शुद्धं शुद्धजाम्बुनदं सुत ।। 13 ।।

इति स्वं (स्वर्णतंत्र) अष्टमः ।।

सिद्धस्वर्णस्य कल्पं तु कथ्यते शृणु सांप्रतं ।
सिद्ध स्वर्णं कल्पतरूवंगरीतालकेश्वरः ।। 1 ।।
(कल्पतरूवगोरितालकेश्वरः)

धातुवेधी पञ्चमस्तु पर्यायाः पञ्च कीर्त्तिताः ।
कर्नाटवोगरी ख्यातः सिद्धस्वर्णस्तु चोत्तरे[10] ।। 2 ।।

पुर्वस्यां तालकः प्रोक्तो धातुवेधी तु पश्चिमे ।
स्वर्गे तु कल्पवृक्षस्तु पञ्च-नाम समन्वितः ।। 3 ।।

षष्ठस्तु स्वर्णविमला तरूरित्य (अ)भिघियते ।
शर्कर कन्दवत् पत्रं पुष्पं कार्पाससमन्निभम् ।। 4 ।।

लवालमानं[11] तत् पुष्प फल चालौकिकं[12] मतम ।
शाखा सव्रो (?) विप्रेन्द्र पुनः शखं प्रवापयेत् ।। 5 ।।

पुर्नवृक्षो भवेत्पुत्र तत् योगं श्रृणु यत्नतः ।
तस्य पत्ररसेनैव धातुमात्रप्रवेधकृत ।। 6 ।।

तस्य पुष्परसेनैव पारदो मृतिमेष्यति ।
हरितालादयः सर्वे मृर्तिभवति सर्वथा ।। 7 ।।

तत्फलं तु समादाय तद्रसं ... यत्नेन गृहेत ।
रसेन खलनं कार्यं पारदस्य त्रियामकम ।। 8 ।।

तं पारदं मुषिकायां हटाग्निं दापयेत सुत ।
मुषिकाग्निप्रदानेन पारदौ मृत्युमान्पुयात् ।। 9 ।।

तस्य संभक्षणात्पुत्र कामरूपी भवेद (त) ध्रुवम ।
पुन (द ?) ता भविष्यति कृष्ण ... (कृष्ण केशी ?)[13] भवेत सुत ।। 10 ।।
धातुमात्रे पारदस्तु लक्षवेधी भवेत ध्रुवम् ।
तस्य पत्ररसेनैवं यामाष्टकं खलेत् ।। 11 ।।

शरावसंपुटे कृत्वा तत्ताल मृत्युज ददेत् ।
पुटं गजा रवं[14] हे राम दध्या चैव प्रयत्नतः ।। 12 ।।

तस्य प्रभक्षणात् पुत्र रूद्धा[15] एवं (?) न (ना ?) शयः ।
धातुमात्रे तु तं दद्यात शतवेधी भवेत ध्रुवम ।। 13 ।।

तत्फलस्य रसं गृह्य ताम्रद्रावे विनिक्षिपेत ।
तताम्रं जायते शुद्धं स्वर्णं जाम्बुनदप्रभ ॥ 14 ॥

तत्फलस्य रसं गृह्य वंगे नागे विनिक्षिपेत ।
तत्तारं जायते शुद्धं कुन्दपुष्पसमप्रभं ॥ 15 ॥

एवं धातुमात्रेण तत्फलस्य रसं सुत ।
तत्क्षणात वेद्यमायाति स्वर्णं स्वर्णत्वमान्पुयात्[8] ॥ 16 ॥

रौप्यं रौप्यत्वमायाति शतवेधी भवेत सुत ।
इति स्वर्णं वोगरिकल्पः ॥

अथ दग्घरूहेः कल्पं श्रृणु यत्नेन साम्प्रतम ।
तत्काष्ठं तु समादायदयग्निमध्ये[16] विनिक्षिपेत ॥ 1 ॥

सचांगारो भवेत पुत्र तदगारं तु वापयेत् ।
अंगारो वृक्ष तां याति तं वृक्ष संग्रहेत सुत ॥ 2 ॥

तत्पञ्चांगारंसंगृह्य पारदे तालके यथा,
एक विंशत् पुढं दद्यात् ततो मृत्युर्भविष्यति ॥ 3 ॥

तद्वयं तु समानीय धातुमात्रे विनिक्षिपेत ।
तत्क्षणाद्वेध्यामायाति (ध्मायाति) धातवः सुरपुजितः ॥ 4 ॥

(तत् काष्ठं) तत्काष्ठं मुषिकां कृत्वा तत्र ताम्रं विनिक्षिपेत् ।
तदग्नौ तु तदा दध्यात् स्वर्णतां याति निश्चितम् ॥ 5 ॥

अंगार चुर्णं निर्गंतु शतांशत प्रवेधकम ।
तप्तं चागरसं पुत्र धातुमात्रेविनिक्षिपेत् ॥ 6 ॥

रौप्यं रौपत्व[17] मायाति[18] स्वर्णं स्वर्णत्वमाययु ।
शुद्धसूतं समादाय तत्मुषायां विनिक्षिपेतं ॥ 7 ॥

Foot Notes

1. "खर्पर"—is the same as "रसक" or calamine.
2. "उदर समा"—here "Udara" could be read as "उदार" which means 'noble' (MW, 185) indicating the use of pure mercury. But it may also mean 'the thick part of anything' as used in Suśruta Samhitā (MW, 184), *i.e.*, the thickest deposit of mercury.
3. "ततश्चरेत"—This word is not clear and does not make proper sense. But the description could indicate that the 'mudra' was floating in mercury in the iron saucer.

4. "क (...)"— The word cannot be deciphered from the manuscript. Probably the first letter of the name of an ingredient.
5. "(कटुकुष्मान्डकल्प :)"—The margins of the MS on the left hand before the word स्वर्णकल्पः has the written note कटुकुष्मान्डकल्पः।
6. "वनोपलायास्तंगारं"—can be broken as वन उपलाया स्त अंगारं। the indication is for the use of forest, stone fuel.
7. "शवके" would be शरावके meaning container. "शरावके"—Here in the śloka two containers are indicated – a saucar and its lid – which are closed together. A type of container is specified : Kukkutaputa.
8. "वंशागारेण" refers to fire fuelled by bamboo and "वनोपलप्रयोगत" might be read as "वन उपल प्रयोगत"—discussed in ch. 5.
9. "प्रस्य" might be read as प्रेष्ठ or प्रेस्य in meaning and use of these terms have been discussed in chapter 5.
10. "चोत्तरे" might be read as च उत्तरे।
11. "लवालमानं" might be read as लवलीमान।
12. "चालौकिंक" might be broken as च अलौकिक।
13. "कृष्ण" could probably mean "कृष्ण केशी"।
14. "पुटं गज" refers to the "गजपुट" as described by Mira Roy and B.V. Subbarayappa, Rasarnavaklpa, New Delhi, 1993 reprint, Glossary, 136, as a square pit filled with cow dung cake used as a fire pit.
15. "रूद्धा" means obstruction and there is reference of रूद्धामुत्रा in Suśrutā Saṁhita as retention of urine, meaning obstruction in urinal passage.
16. "समादायदयग्निमध्ये" might be read as समादयात अग्निमध्ये।
17. "चागरसं" might be च अंगार रसं।
18. "रौपत्वमायाति" in the hand—written manuscript could also stand for "रौपत्वमायाति"—Monier Williams Dictionary, 142, describes आप्नयति as to cause, to reach, to obtain or to gain.

English Transcription: Suvarnatantra

Śrī Gaṇeśāya Namaḥ.
Śrī Paraśurāma Uvāca.
Devadeva Mahādeva ṛdhi buddhi phala prada.
Pūrvam Saṁsuchitā ṛdhi rasāyanparā varā.[1]
Yasyāḥ Sādhanamātreṇa svarāt tulyô narô bhavet.
Tāṁ siddhiṁ vada me deva yadittam bhaktavatsalaḥ.[2]
Pūrvaṁ tu Kathitaṁ deva ratna tantraṁ tvayā mama.
Guṭikāḥ Kathitam pūrvam sahasradvitayaṁ Śiva.[3]
Pāradāḥ Kathitaṁ ṣaṭaśata mṛtirūpakāḥ.
Dhātunāmaṣṭakalpāstu pūrvameva prakāśitāḥ.[4]
Dhāturyogākhya Kalpāstu pūrva meva prakāśitāḥ.
Ratnānāṁ Karaṇe tantraṁ pūrvameva prakāśitam.[5]
Śrī dhātukaraṇe taṇtraṁ pūrva meva prākaśitam.
Haritālastu Kathitaḥ śatasaptaprabhedataḥ.[6]
Kintu svarṇākhyātantraṁ tu na ṁahya kathitaṁ prabhô.
Kaśyapena maheśān bhartsiasmi Maheśvara.[7]
Bhūmidānam mayā dattamṛṣye Kasyapāya vai.
Kaśyapenāpyahaṁ prôktô bhūmibhāgaṁ tyaja prabhô.[8]
Sthānārthaṁ tu Maheśān ratnābdhiḥ prārthitô mayā.
Vāṇamātraṁ sthalam tena dattaṁ mama Maheśvara.[9]
Sthānaṁ prāptaṁ Maheśān bhakṣaṇaṁ mama nāsti vai.
Bhakṣaṇam dehi me deva yadi putrasama Śaṁkara.[10]

Īs'vara uvāca.

Śrṇu Rāma prabakṣyāmi rahasyāti rahasyakam.
Svarnataṇtrābhidhaṁ tantraṁ kalpa rūpeṇa kathyate.[11]
Tatrādou svarṇatantrasya Kalpaṁ śrṇu suputraka.
Tailakandabhidha kandaḥ siddha kandaḥ Prakīrtitaḥ.[12]
Kandaḥ Kamalavatjñeyaḥ patrāṇi Kañjavatddhiśô.
Tathaiva tu mahāpatraṁ tailam sravati sarvadā.[13]
Jalamadhyaṁ sadā putra baryaiva (i) pratiṣṭhati.
Viṣa kandeti vikhyataḥ viṣaṣṭaka vināśat(n)aḥ.[14]
Tailasrāvī mahākandaḥ paritô(s)tailavajjakaṁ.

Daśahastamite (R) rāma paritastailavajjaḷaṁ.[15]
Mahaviṣadharaḥ putra tadadhô vasati dhruvam.
Kandādhaḥ Kandachāyātu nanyatra gacchati priya.[16]
Tat parīkṣā vidhāy(n)ādou kande sūcīm praveśayet.
Sucīm drāvāknṣnāt putra (sutra) tat kandam tu samaharet.[17]
Tatkandaṁ tu samādāya śuddha sūtam Khalet tridhā (?).
Muṣāya nikṣipettam tu tattailam tatra nikṣipet.[18]
Dīpāgni tu mahārāma vaṁsāgāreṇa (vaṁśāṁgāreṇa) dīpayet.
Tatkṣaṇāt mrtimāyāti lakṣavedhī bhavet suta.[19]
Tataḥ prabhakṣayedrāma Kṣunnidrāhārakô dhruvam.
Tālam śuddhoṁ samānīya tattailena Khalet suta.[20]
Saptadhā pratyahaṁ (R)rāma tevaṁ viṁśaddinaṁ dhruvam.
Haritalô mṛtidheti nirdhumô jāyate dhruvam.[21]
Agnou putra tatô dadhā nirdhūmô jāyate suta.
Tattalām chāṣṭaṁ dhātou tu dadhyādrāvakate (dadhyādrāve kṛta) sati.[22]
Sarvavedhī bhabedeva śatavedhī bhave (*t*) dhruvam.
Tattailaṁ tu samādāya tatra tāmra drāve vinikṣipet.[23]
Tatkṣaṇāt tāmra vedhasyā divyam bhavati kāñcanam.
Vange kāṁsye yadā dadhyātadā roupyam bhavet suta.[24]
Tamram lôhe tathā rītyāṁ tāre Khaparasutake (kharpara sutake)[1].
Tatkṣanādroupyamāyāti divyaṁ bhavati Kāñcanam.[25]
Udarasamā pārada[2] tu samānīya (samādāya) vilakṣaṇaḥ.
Chāyāyāṁ Khalanaṁ kāryamekaviṁśadinam suta.[26]
Louhaṁ yantre tatô dadhyāt pāradasya rasasaṁyuta.
Ubhou samānabhāgou sthāllou mudrāṁ tataścaret[3].[27]
Tatô ghorāsya mudrā(*ṁ*) tudadhyāt(?)tadho(?)krame(Krameṇaca) ca.
Tadhatra chullikāyāṁ tu sthāpayed (*t*) yatnena (yatnata) suta.[28]
Tatra śaṁkuniveśyāya tadyantram tatra vadhayet.
Ādou dīpāgnimārabhya haṭāgni dāpayetataḥ.[29]
Śrī Puraścharyā putô mantra svarṇāṁakarṣaṇ purvakaṁ.
Braḥmacharya parôbhutvā tatrāgniṁ dāpayet suta.[30]
Arnyāgniṁ tu vaṁśāgni khadire cātha putraka.
Māsamātre vyatīte tu Kalāmātra prajāyate.[31]
Uḍḍīya prathamaṁ (R) rāma mudrāyā gacchati dhruvaṁ.
Adhôyāti tataḥ sutaḥ tatra śabdaṁ Karôti hi.[32]
Atra śabdo bhavet putra ka (?)[4] tatra samādiśet.

Ka (?) tatra prada śobhātu na anu bhakṣanārtha prayojyapet (prayojayet).[33]

Sudhākaraḥ (rah) Kāma (Kāṁsa) (Kāri)? (Vogari/vangari)? sarvathā bhavati dhruvam.

Kalāmśaṁśa yukto hi śatavedhī bhavet dhruvam.[34]

Evam dvādaśamāsaṁ tamāgni deyo dvijottama.[35]

Tatkandacchāyāvṛkṣe tu sadā tiṣṭhati putraka (putra)?

Iti saṁkṣepataḥ prôktôḥ Kimanyat śrutamichhyasi.

Iti Svarṇatantre Śiva Paraśurāma Saṁvāde tailakanda Kalpaḥ.

Rama Uvāca.

Kaṭu Kuṣmāṇḍa Kalpo hi Suchitam Kathaya prabhô.

Śiva, (Uvāca)

Kaṭu kuṣumāṇḍamādāyatadrasam grāhayet śuddhoḥ.[1]

Vaṁge dadhyātadā putra roupyam prajāyate.

Tāmralôhe tathā rītyā ṭaṁkaṇaṁ tadrasaṁkṣipet.[2]

Tatkṣaṇāt svarṇatô yāti svarṇa jāmbu nadaṁ bhavet.

Tadrase tārasaṁyuktam saptadhatum khalet suta.[3]

Evam muni (?) dinaṁ putro Khalitva tu punaḥ punaḥ.

Kalaṁkastu bhavet śuddho śatavedhī bhavet suta.[4]

Iti Svarṇa Kalpaḥ (Katukuṣmāṇḍa Kalpaḥ).[5]

Athanyam saṁpravakṣyāmi Rāmasāvahitô bhava.

Raktabījakaṭu gṛhya ṛddhivalyabhidhô suta.[1]

Tāmram saṁśodhya yatnena tattāmra tu saṁkṣipet.

Tattāmram Svarṇānām yāti gangeya bhavati dhruvam.[2]

Jalaṁ vaṁsye kṛtvādou rasaṁtatra vinikṣipet.

Tatkṣaṇādroupya tāṁ yāti kundapuṣpa samaprabham.[3]

Tadroupya tu samādāya tadrasena tu saṁkhalet.

Dinaikaṁ tu khalet putrakalaṁko bhavati dhruvam.[4]

Tat Kalaṁkam tu samārattikārdhyam dvijôttama.

Dhātumātre vinikṣipya rakśmivedhī bhavet suta.[5]

Iti Svarṇa Kalpaḥ (Kaṭuraktabija)

Athanyatyasaṁ pravaksyāmi.

Kaṭu tumbābhidhaṁ suta.

Katu tumbi vane gattvā mantra prārthena purvakaṁ.[1]

Vīja sāra kaṭu deva dṛṣṭe tu vadanam katutva.

Ida śaṣya tu kalpôhi kārya yatnena mata.[2]

Sūcikā pīttalānām cha vavah kāryet suta.

Karttike samanuprāpte phale sūchīṁ praveśayet.[3]

Yuttsyā praveśa ya kārya bījavedho yathana cha.

Pancacattvāraḥ saṣthaḥ saptāṣṭho nava vā priya.[4]

Amāghasya samādhya taṁ phalāni cha avalokayet.

Vijaṁvadhe samutpanne phalaṁ naśyati tu dhruvam.[5]

Trimāsam tatra śayanaṁ kāryaṁ yatnena dhīmatā.

Yadhyat phalaṁ bhavenaṣṭaṁ tattatyājyaṁ tataḥ suta.[6]

Tadrasena tu sā sūchyaḥ siddhā eva bhavanti hi.

Masottaraṁ Paraśurāma teṣām niṣkāsanaṁ charet.[7]

Sūchīnam (*a*) gni saṁyogaḥ kāryaśchāmnā yayogataḥ.

Vanôpalāyāṣṭaṁgāraṁ[6] (*a*) Kṛtvā caiva śarāvake.[8]

Tatra sūchyastu nikṣipya svarṇaṁ bha(va) ti Kāñcanam.

Śaṛāvadvayasaṁrūddh (hā) sūchyaḥ kāryā (*h*) prayatnataḥ.[9]

Kukkuṭākhyaputenaiva Kṛtvā caiva śa(rā) vake.[7]

Bhavejjāmbunadaprabhaṁ vaṁśāgāreṇa[8] vadeyaṁ. Vanopalāproyogataḥ.[10]

Athavā muṣikāṁ dattvā tatra deyātu sūchikā.

Tatra dhmātô Maheśaiṣta divyaṁ bhavati Kāñcanam.[11]

Iti Svarṇatantra kaṭutumbik (alpasya) chaturthaḥ.

Athānyat saṁpravakṣyāmi siddhatumbī śrīsusiddhidāṁ.

Adou vaṁgaṁ suśôdhāyaḥ muṣikāyaṁ vinikṣipet.[1]

Śvetā tu girikarṇo tu yôṇivalyamidhāṁ suta.

Tadrasam tatra nikṣipyadhame yatnena puṁgava.[2]

Tadvanga jāyate śuddhaṁ Kuda (kunda) puṣpa sama prabhaṁ.

Iti Svarṇa pañcamaḥ.[11]

Athānyat pravaksyāmi śvetagkṣuraka Kalapakaṁ.

Yena vijñānmātrena rasāyanavarā bhavet.[1]

Vaṁgaṁ saṁśodhya yatnena tatrakṣurajarasaṁ.

Nikṣipya pradhamet (?) putra vaṁgastāruttvatāṁ tyājet.[1]

Iti ṣaṣṭhaḥ.

Athānyat sampravakṣyāmi śvetourandasya Kalpakaṁ.
Svetourandasya mūlaṁ tu gṛhīttvā puṣya bhāskare.[1]
Tattailena sughṛṣṭam tu karpureṇa samnvitaṁ.
Añjannetrayugalaṁ saptapātāladarśanaṁ.[2]
Siddhānjānjānamidam siddhaṁ siddhayôga vinirmitam.
Tanmūlamārgapāṣānaṁ śuddhasuta samanvitam.[3]
Kṛṣṭa chadrāvasaṁpiṣṭaṁ śuddham muṣā gataṁ dhayet.
Śālmalī Khadiraṁgāroustridhāvaṁge bhavatyalam.[4]
Aṅgāramadhya suchinam sthāpanam tu samācharet.
Dhyāmatam bhavati Viprendra divyam bhavati Kancanam.[12]
Tad vaṁgeṣu drutou Kṣipraṁ Sahaśrāṁsa Vedhakam.
Vījaṁ śvetaṁ tathā puṣpa madhyasya śveta evahi.[5]
Vījaṁ raktaṁ tathā puṣpaṁ phalaṁ raktaṁ prakīrtitaṁ.
Tat Kalpaḥ śvetavajñeyaḥ sarvasiddhipra vataḥ.[6]
Iti saptamaḥ. (Iti svarṇatantre rakta kalpaḥ saptamaḥ).

Kākari Kalpaṁ deveśa śrṇu yatnena sāmpratam.
Kākarih kākaṁ tu śabdou vai paryāyavāchakou.[1]
Puṣyārka phalaṁ gṛhya supakkam sumanôharam.
Tat phalasya rasenaiva pāradaṃ sudriḍa khalet.[2]
Dinamātram khaleddeva baddho bhavati pāradaḥ.
Evaṁ viṁśaddinaṁ deva tadrasena tu melayet.[3]
Rasa saṃmelanāt eva guṭiṣaṣṭhimukha mata.
Tasyāh sandhāraṇā ... ṣaṣthisiddheśvaro bhavet.[4]
Tatpañcāṅgārasanaiva pārada saṁkhalet suta.
Taṁ muṣikāyāṁ nikṣipya taṁ rasaṁ tu punardadet.[5]
Evaṁ praharamātre tu tadrasam tatra nikṣipya.
Evaṁ krameṇa satputra pāradou mṛtimeṣyati.[6]
Taṁ pāradaṁ tu satputra rattikadaśa saṁmāsakaṁ.
Bhakṣayet yatnataḥ putra chirañjīvī bhavet suta.[7]
Valipalitānirmukto kāmarūpi bhavet sa tu.
Tathaiva prasya (preṣṭa or presya)[9] sahasrasaṁbhakṣa bhavetyeva naraḥ suta.[8]

Haritāla tadrasam tu dattvā tu khalenaṁ charet.

Yāmāṣṭou saṁkhalet putra nirdhumo bhavati dhruvam.[9]

Rattikārdhyam bhakṣayetam gunaḥ pāradavad bhavet.

Taṁ pāradaṁ tu Kanake lakṣavedhī bhavet suta.[10]

Tathaiva tālakaḥ putro śatavedhī prajāyate.

Taṁ patrasya rasam putro vaṁgamadhye vinikṣipet.[11]

Tattāraṁ jāyate śuddham Kundapuṣpasamaprabham.

Tasya puṣpa rasaḥ putra dhātumātra pravedhakṛta.[12]

Tatphalasya rasaṁ putra tāmra drāve vinikṣipet.

Suvarṇa jāyate śuddham śuddhajāmbunadam suta.[13]

Iti svaṁ (svarṇatantra) aṣṭamaḥ.

Siddhasvarṇasya Kalpaṁ tu kathyate sṛṇu sāmpratam.

Siddha svarṇam Kalpataru vôgari tālakeśvaraḥ.[1]

Dhātuvedhī pañcamastu paryāyāḥ pañca kīrtitāḥ.

Karṇātavôgari khyātaḥ siddhasvarṇastu chôttare[10].[2]

Purvasyam tālakaḥ prôktô dhātuvedhī tu paśchime.

Svarge tu kalpavṛkṣastu pañca-nāma samanvitaḥ.[3]

Ṣaṣṭhastu svarṇavimalā tarūritya(ā)bhidhayate.

Sarkarākandavatr patraṁ puṣpaṁ kārpāsasannibham.[4]

Lavālamānam[11] tat puṣpa phala chaloukikam[12] matam.

Śākhā satro (?) Viprendra punaḥ śākham pravāpayet.[5]

Punarvṛkṣô bhavetputra tat yogaṁ sṛṇu yatnataḥ.

Tasya patrarasenaiva dhātumātrapravedhakṛta.[6]

Tasya puṣpa rasenaiva pāradô mṛtimeṣyati.

Haritāladayaḥ sarve mṛtirbhavati sarvathā.[7]

Tatphalaṁ tu samādāya tadrasam... yatnena gṛhet.

Rasena khalanaṁ kāryam pāradasya triyāmakam.[8]

Taṁ pāradaṁ muṣikāyāṁ haṭāgniṁ dāpayet suta.

Muṣikāgnipradānena pāradou mṛtyumāpnuyāt.[9]

Tasya saṁbhakṣanāt putra kāmarūpī bhaved (*t*) dhruvam.

Puna (*d* ?) ta bhaviṣyati *kṛṣṇa*.... (kṛṣṇa Kesī ?)[13] bhavet suta.[10]

Dhātumātre pāradastu lakṣavedhī bhavet dhruvam.

Tasya patrarasenaivaṁ yāmāṣṭakam khalet.[11]

Sarāvasaṁpuṭe kṛtvā tattāla mṛtyuja dadet.
Puṭam gajāravaṁ[14] he Rāma dadhyā caiva prayatnataḥ.[12]
Tasya prabhakṣaṇāt putra rūddhā[15] eva (?) na (nā ?) śayaḥ.
Dhātumātre tu taṁ dadhyāt śatavedhī bhavet dhruvam.[13]
Tatphalasya rasaṁ gṛhya tāmradrāve vinikṣipet.
Tatāmram jāyate śuddhaṁ svarṇam jāmbunnada prabha.[14]
Tatphalasya rasaṁ gṛhya vaṁge nāge vinikṣipet.
Tattāram jāyate śuddhaṁ kundapuṣpasamaprabhaṁ.[15]
Evaṁ dhātumātreṇa tat phalasya rasaṁ suta.
Tatkaṣaṇāt vedhamāyāti svarṇam svarṇatvamāpnuyāt.[16]
Roupya roupyatvamāyāti śatavedhī bhavet suta.
Iti svarṇam vôgarikalpaḥ.

Atha dagdharūheḥ kalpaṁ śṛṇu yatnena ṣāmpratam.
Tatkāṣṭhaṁ tu samādāyadāgnimadhye[16] vinikṣipet.[1]
Sachaṅgāro bhavet putra tadaṅgāram tu vāpayet.
Aṅgāro vṛkṣe tāṁ yāti taṁ vṛkṣa saṁgrahet suta.[2]
Tatpañcāṅgārasaṁgṛhya pārade tālake yathā.
Eka viṁśat puṭam dadhyāt tato mṛtyurbhaviṣyati.[3]
Tadvayaṁ tu samānīya dhātumātre vinikṣipet.
Tatkṣaṇadvedhamāyāti dhātavaḥ surapujitaḥ.[4]
(Tat kāṣṭhaṁ) tatkāṣṭha muṣikam kṛtvā tatra tāmram vinikṣipet.
Tadagnou tu tadā dadhyāt svarṇatāṁ yāti niśchitam.[5]
Aṅgāra churnam nirgantuṁ śatāṁśata pravedhakam.
Taptaṁ chāṅgarasaṁ[17] putra dhātumātrevinikṣipet.[6]
Roupyam roupyatvatamāyāti[18] svarṇam Svarṇatvamāyāya.
Śuddhasutaṁ samādāya tatmuṣāyāṁ vinikṣipetaṁ.[7]

Foot Notes

1. "Kharpara"—is the same as "rasaka" or calamine.
2. "Udara Sama"—"Udara" could be read as "udāra" meaning noble (Monier Williams, 185) indicating the use of pure mercury. But it may also mean "udara" or the "thick part of anything"—as used in Suśruta Saṁhitā (MW, 184), *i.e.*, the thickest deposit of mercury.

3. "Tataścharet"—this word is not clear and does not make proper sense.
4. "Ka—(...)"—the word cannot be deciphered. Probably the first letter of the name of an ingredient.
5. "(Kaṭukuṣmāṇḍakalpaḥ)"—the margins of the MS. on the left hand before the word svarṇakalpaḥ has the written note kaṭukuṣmāṇḍakalpaḥ).
6. "Vanôpalāyāṣṭaṁgāraṁ" can be broken as vaṇa Upalāyā sta Aṅgāraṁ—meaning the use of forest stone as fuel.
7. "Śavake" would be śarāvake meaning container. Here two parts—a container and a lid are indicated specified as Kukkuṭa Puṭa.
8. "Vaṁśogāreṇa" would be vaṁśāṅgāreṇa and "vanopalāprоyogata" might be read as vano Upalā prayogata.
9. "Prasya" might be read as pręṣṭa or presya. Meaning and use of these terms have been discussed in chapter 5.
10. "Chôttare" might be read as cha uttare.
11. "Lavālāmāna" might be read as Lavalīmāna.
12. "Chaloukika" might be read as cha aloukika.
13. "Kṛṣṇa" could be a reference to kṛṣṇā-Keśī.
14. "Gajaravam" might refer to a special container for heating or storing.
15. "Ruddhā" means obstruction and there is reference of ruddhāmutra in Suśtruta Saṁhitā as retention of urine.
16. "Samādāyadayāgnimadhye" might be read as samādāyat agnimadhya.
17. "Chāgārasaṁ" might be read as cha aṅgāra rasam.
18. "Roupatvamāyāti" could be read as "roupatvamāpnayati". Monier Williams Dictionary, describes āpnayati as to cause, to reach, to obtain or to gain.

3

TRANSLATION OF SUVARNATANTRA

I bow to Śrī Gaṇeśa, Śrī Paraśurāma said: O Mahādeva, God of Gods,Bestower of prosperity, intelligence and (good) results! You have earlier related that prosperity of the supreme Rasāyana, by achieving which, man becomes the equal of Indra . If you love your disciple, O Lord, narrate to me that success.1-2 Lord! You have earlier narrated to me the Ratnatantra,'O Śiva ! You have earlier related the two thousand gutikās. 3. You have narrated mercury with six hundred forms of death. You have previously revealed the eight kalpas of the metals. 4. You have earlier revealed the kalpas named Dhāturyôga. You have revealed the tantra for making jewels. 5. You have narrated the tantra for making śrīdhātu. You have narrated haritāla with its seven hundred varieties. 6. But you have not related to me, O Lord, the tantra named svarna. O Maheśvara! I was reprimanded(?) by Kaśyapa.7. I gave my land to the sage Kaśyapa. Lord! Kaśyapa told me: "Give up part of your land". 8. O Maheśvara (?) For the sake of land (?), I asked for the ocean of jewels. Mahesvara! He gave me land of only an arrow's length.9. Maheṣa ! I obtained land, but did not get food(?). O Śankara! Grant me food(?) if I be your son.10. The Lord said: Listen O Rāma, I will speak the mystery of mysteries. I will relate the tantra named Svarṇatantra in kalpas (chapters). 11. My good son! Listen first to the (first) kalpa of Svarṇatantra. The bulb named tailakanda (oily bulb) is said to be siddhakanda. 12. The bulb is like the (bulb of the) lotus, and its leaves like.....(?).Thus the large leaf always exudes oil. 13. My son! It is always in the water, it is settled in water(?). It is known as visakanda (Poisonous stalk) and destroys the twenty-eight. 14. The great bulb exudes oil in the water all around for ten arms's lengths, and the water appears like spread of oil, son. 15. My son! Under it, a venomous snake certainly dwells. My dear! The shadow of the bulb does not go anywhere from under it (?) 16. To test it, you first insert a needle into it. My son! The needle will immediately dissolve....(?) 17. Having procured this bulb, rub it with mercury in a mortar three times. Then throw it into a crucible as well as the oil .18. O Rāma! Light a lamp(?) with the embers of bamboo, and heat it. Immediately it (the mercury) is killed, and acquires the property of converting one hundred thousand times its own weight of the base metal into gold.19. O Rāma! When fed to one, it certainly impairs appetite and sleep. Son!pure tāla should be brought and rubbed in a mortar with this oil.20. O Rāma! If haritāla (is rubbed) with this every day for twenty days, it is killed and will certainly become smokeless.(?). 21. Son! Then if it is placed in the fire, it becomes smokeless.This tāla should be thrown into eight molten metals. 22. It dissolves........(?) the metals........... and renders purified metals(?) This oil should be taken and thrown into molten copper. 23. Immediately, the copper being purified .... (?) turns into excellent gold. If it is thrown into tin and bell-metal, they turn into silver, son. 24. In the same way, thrown into copper and iron.....(?) zinc, immediately turns into excellent gold. 25. My son! The expert should take the mercury inside and rub it in a mortar for twenty days in the shade. 26. The mercury should then be put in an iron machine (?) (yantra could also be a device) .....(?), both in equal quantities, the iron will then turn into......(?). 27. Then the mudra named Ghorā should be put (?) in........ (?) in turn. O Son! Then it (the yantra) should be carefully placed on the oven by inserting it with the help of a śaṅku or ghomon. 28. There (?) will expand the machine (?) Starting first with the lamp-fire, one should place it in brightly burning....(?) fire. 29. My son! It first....(?) then.....(?) should be put in fire, practising celibacy. 30. My son! Use Forest fire, bamboo fire all the while khadira wood, only a part of which grows in a month (?). 31. or Flying first Rāma, goes certainly to mudrā(?). Then it falls, mixed,(?) thus and makes a sound. 32. Where the sound occurs, son, who would direct one there(?) ......(?) should not be given to eat. 33. It brightens, works (creates brass)? or orpiment? always pure.........(?) always fulfils one's desire. A part joined to a part takes on the property a hundred-fold of its own property. 34. O Foremost Brāhmaṇa! It should be placed in the fire thus for twelve months. 35. ....(?) always remain under the large tree from that bulb, son. This is related briefly, what else do you wish to hear? 36. Here ends the chapter on oil bulb in the conversation between Śiva and Paraśurāma in Svarṇatantra.

× × × × ×

Rama said: O Lord ! Narrate the chapter on Kaṭukuṣmāṇḍa. Siva said: ....(?) must procure Kaṭukuṣmāṇḍa and take its juice. 1. My Son! When it is put in tin, silver is created. In the same way, placed in copper and iron, ...(?). 2. It at once turns into gold, and the gold becomes jāmbunada. Son! Its juice along with .....(?) should be rubbed in a mortar with seven metals. 3. Thus, Son, ...(?) again and again, a flow appears, and it takes on a hundred fold the properties. 4. Here ends the chapter on Kaṭukuṣmāṇḍa in Svarṇatantra.

× × × × ×

Now I will relate another (subject), Rāma, pay attention. My Son! taking Raktabījakaṭu, which is known as enhancing prosperity (?), and after purifying copper with care., throw the juice into this copper. The copper will surely turn into Gāṅgeya gold. 1-2. Putting......(?) in water, throw the juice into it. Immediately it will turn into the colour of kunda flower. 3. O Foremost Brāḥmaṇa! Taking half a rattikā of that silver, and throwing it in any metal, will become...........(?), Son. 4. Here ends the chapter on Katuraktabīja in Svarṇatantra.

× × × × ×

Now I will relate another (chapter) named Kaṭutumbī (bittergourd?), my son! Going to the forest of Kaṭutumbī, after spells and prayer, if bitter seeds (?) are seen.... (?) such a one should be cut with care(?). 1-2. My son! You must make many needles of copper and zinc alloy (?) When (the month of kārttika) arrives, insert the needle in the fruit. 3. .....(?) insert it so it does not pierce the seed- four, five, six, seven, eight or nine, my dear. 4. Up until Māgha, watch the fruits(?). If the seeds are pierced, the fruit will certainly be destroyed.5. The intelligent should lie there with care for three months. My son ! The fruits that are destroyed should be discarded.6. The needles are steeped (?) in that juice. O Paraśurāma ! They should be extracted after a month. 7. The needles should be set on fire according to the texts, by (lighting a fire) of embers of forest stone (?) in an earthen dish. 8. There the needles thrown in become gold. The needles should be shut up between two dishes with care. 9. Placing it in a dish with a cover (?) named Kukkuṭa, it becomes the colour of Jāmbunada with bamboo embers, by applying forest stones(?) 10. Or else it should be placed in a crucible and the needle placed therein. Swollen there, Maheśa (?) it becomes excellent gold.11. The needles should be placed in the middle of embers, O Foremost Brāḥmaṇa! Then swollen up, it becomes excellent gold. Here ends the fourth chapter named Kaṭutumbī in Svarṇatantra.

× × × × ×

Now I will narrate another (chapter) on Siddhatumbī, which gives success. First purify tin and throw it in a crucible. 1. My son ! Then śveta, girikarṇi and that (?) named yôṇivalli (should be taken) and their juice thrown in it and roasted (?) with care, Foremost man ! From there evolves pure tin the colour of kunda flowers. 2. Here ends the fifth chapter named Siddhatumbī in Svarṇatantra.

× × × × ×

Now I will relate another chapter on Śvetagokṣura, which, if it is but known, becomes the supreme medicine. 1. Purifying tin with care, throw gokṣura dust in it and roast it, son. The tin will give up.......(?).2. Here ends the sixth chapter named śvetagokṣura in Svarṇatantra.

× × × × ×

Now I will relate another chapter on śveta eraṇḍa. Taking the root of the śvetaraiṇḍa when the sun is in the Puṣyā house, rub its oil with camphor, and anoint the eyes with it- it will show one the seven pātālas or the mythical netherworlds. 1-2. This is siddhāñjana, pure and made by magic (?). The Pāṣāṇbheda, its root (?) , with pure mercury, ground with the juice of Kuṣta (?) .....(?) should be roasted in a crucible with the embers of śālmalī and khadira (trees) three times, when it turns into tin. 3-4. Thrown into the molten tin, it takes on a thousandth part (?) The seed is white, so is the centre of the flower. The seed is red, so is the flower and fruit said to be. This chapter is to be known as similar to the white, and grants total success. Here ends the seventh chapter named śvetaraṇḍa in Suvarṇatantra.

× × × × ×

O King of Gods (?) Now listen carefully to the chapter on Kākari. The words kākari and kāka are synonymous. 1. When the sun is in the Puṣyā constellation, take the ripe and beautiful fruit and with its juice, rub mercury firmly in a mortar. 2. O Lord, rubbed for a day, the mercury hardens (?) . Thus for twenty days, it should be mixed with the juice. By this mixing of the juice, guṭiṣaṣṭhimūkha is obtained. With its......(?) ....(?) becomes ṣaṣṭhiśiddheśvara (or attains a high quality?)...............(?)......... 3-4.

My son! Rub the mercury in a mortar with the juice of five parts(?) Then again place it in a crucible and again put in the juice. 5. My good son! For a prahara, put that juice there. In this way, the mercury is killed. 6. My good son! Taking about a rattikā of this mercury if one feeds somebody on it with care, this person lives for ever. 7. He has no wrinkles, his hair does not turn white, he becomes handsome, if a man eats a thousand prasyas (preṣṭhas?) of this, son. 8. This juice should be placed in haritāla and rubbed in a mortar for eight yāmas, son, whereupon it becomes smokeless. 9. If half a rattikā is fed to someone, that has the equality / attributes of mercury. That mercury in gold takes on hundred thousand times its quality, son. 10. Thus the tālaka, son, takes on hundred times its quality. The juice of that leaf, son, should be thrown in (molten) tin. 11.Then pure tāla (?) is created, the colour of kunda flower. The juice of that flower will transmute ....(?) any metal. 12. The juice of that fruit, son, thrown in molten copper, son, turns into pure jāmbunada gold. 13. Here ends the eighth chapter named kākari in Svarṇatantra.

× × × × ×

Now listen, I will relate the chapter on pure gold, from the wish-yielding tree, pure gold which is vôgarītālakeśvara. 1. This is about the five kinds of dhātuvedhī famous in five quarters.......(?) It has five names (?) The pure gold in the north is known as Karṇāṭavôgarī. 2. In the east, it is called tālaka, in the west, the transmuting agent or dhatuvedhī.......(?) of metals, in heaven, svarga, it is known as Kalpavrakṣa-these are the five names. 3. The sixth pure gold is called Taru. It has leaves like ....(?) and flower like the kārpāsa.4 This flower is like lavāla.......... (?) and the fruit is said to be super natural. O Foremost Brāḥmaṇa ! The branches may be broken off and replanted. 5. The tree will grow again, son, now listen carefully to its application. The juice of its leaves causes....(?) of any metal. 6., With the juice of its flower , mercury is killed. Haritāla etc are killed in every way. 7. Taking that fruit, take out its juice with care. Mercury should be rubbed in a mortar with this juice for three (nights) yāmas. 8. My son! Put this mercury in a crucible on a ....(?) fire. The mercury will be killed if fire is lighted under the crucible. 9. Fed on this, son, a person becomes handsome, liberal and black-haired.

10. My son ! Mercury takes on hundred thousand the qualities of any metal. Rub it with the juice of its leaf in a mortar for eight yāmas. 11. Placing it in a sealed earthen pot, that tāla should be killed (?) O Rāma ! Carefully put in the pot called gaja (?) 12. Eating it, son, ...(?) without doubt. Placed in any metal it takes on its qualities hundred fold. 13. Taking the juice of that fruit, throw it in molten copper. That copper will become pure gold of the colour of jāmbunada. 14. Taking the juice of that fruit, throw it in tin and ......(?). Then tāla(?) is made the colour of kunda flower. 15. Thus, mixed with any metal, the juice of that fruit , son, immediately takes on its quality, gold becomes gold, silver becomes silver and takes on its quality a hundredfold. 16. Here ends the ninth chapter named vogari in Svarṇatantra.

× × × × ×

Now listen carefully to the chapter on burnt tree...............(?) Taking its wood, throw it in fire. 1. It will burn itself into embers, son, take these embers and plant them (bury them) in soil (?). The embers become a tree. Collect the tree (?) 2. Taking these five embers, place them in mercury and tālaka in twenty-one vessels. Then it is killed. 3. Taking .....(?) throw it into any metal. Immediately, the metals will change (?). 4. Placing the wood in a crucible, throw it into copper. Then set it on the fire, it will certainly turn into gold. 5. The ground embers..... (?) will change a hundredfold. Throw in any metal into the hot ember. 6. Silver will turn into silver, gold into gold, pure mercury should be taken and thrown into a crucible. 7.

× × × × ×

4

SUVARNATANTRA: AN INTERPRETATION

Chittabrata Palit

The text as the name suggests is a treatise on the technology of conversion of baser metals into gold, written or copied from the original by one Raghunāth Śharmā of probably c.16th century. This is in the tail of Nāgārjuna's Rasaratnākara of the 8th century (A.D.) composition dealing with the alchemy of uses of mercury into gold.

What would have been the motivation behind the composition of the treatise? Was it greed of gold to get rich quick? Gold rush is always a primary motivation. But if this is ascribed to the text, the author is unwarrantably undermined. It is better to infer that he was propelled by a desire to discover metallic medicine for the health of mankind and the secrets of metallurgy. This neglected branch of inorganic chemistry has been explored in this work, but when plant and animal substances are mixed with the metal into the compound, there is a fusion of inorganic and organic chemistry.

The author appears to be an expert in metallurgy as well. The text should be read as a manual of chemical technology. One should give the scholar his due. Acharya Prafulla Chandra Ray took due notice of two such manuscripts as this one in his 'History of Hindu Chemistry' and experiment with gold and other metals for proven results in medicine and metallurgy.

The text has got several constraints. The logical sequence is missing or is fragmented. One has to rationalise to get at the meaning. There is a jumble of indigenous words jostling with pure Sanskrit words and much of folk lore is appropriated in this kind of world since the time of Atharva Veda. Metal and plant 'names' are obscure, so also the measures. But my colleague Nupur Dasgupta has tried her best to decipher them in her interpretation. Another version by Ms Sutapa Saha, the Research Scholar associated with the project is also enclosed for continuous reading and analysis. It is difficult to arrive at any formula of metallurgy or medicine in the modern state of the art of science.

There is a lot of referal to Maheśwara as the giver and Paraṣu-rāma as the receiver of knowledge. This religious bonding as in caturvarga also obfuscates the true meaning. There are various versions available in the Asiatic Society, Calcutta and Bhandarkar Research Institute, Pune.

Many of these are mere copies except minor linguistic aberrations. A comparative study with Rasanakṣatramālikā and Rasaratnasamucaya would enhance the value of the present work but art is long and time is short. Please follow the translation and other interpretations to get at what has been stated above.

5

INTERPRETING ŠUVARṆATANTRA

Nupur Dasgupta

Sūvarṇatantra: References from the Asiatic Society MS No: IM 5384.

The particular manuscript from the Asiatic Society (IM 5384) presented in this volume bears the name Suvarṇatantra and contains 4 folios. The manuscript is composed in Sanskrit and the script is Devnāgari. It contains 10 kalpas, which may be treated as expositions or chapters. We have as yet no clue to the exact date of the ms. However, from the name of many of the ingredients that are also found referred in the Rasārṇavakalpa, (1) it seems that the present ms at least follows after Rasārṇavakalpa. The recipes mentioned in this ms match in some parts with those mentioned in the latter ms. However, the use of some terms suggest a much later date. The term *culli,* which occurs in the 18th line of the first *kalpa* obviously does not belong to the Sanskrit vocabulary of earlier times. Culli is defined as a fireplace in the Monier Williams dictionary, where it is pointed out that the word was included by "native lexicons, and has not yet been met with in any published text." (2) Among the lexicographers, this dictionary mentions by name Bhāvaprakāśa of Bhāvamisra, Hemachandra, etc. – all early medieval composers. (3) However, it is clear from the dictionary that this term is not referred in the works of these early medieval lexicographers of up to the 13th century. Thus the current ms was probably not composed before the thirteenth century.

Acharya P.C. Ray in his compendium History of Hindu Chemistry has given a brief review of the scientific discussions contained in two manuscripts named Sûvarṇataṇtra (Benaras ms) and Svarnataṇtra (Dacca ms), which he had consulted. He mentions that these manuscripts were recovered from Benaras and Dacca respectively. The dates of these mss have not been discussed by Acharya Ray. However, he includes the discussions on "Chemistry in Sûvarṇataṇtra" at the end in the section he named "The Tantric Period" in which he includes all mss dated from the 16th century A.D. onwards. (4) Excerpts from these mss in original were also edited and published in the volume II of Ray's compendium. This author went through both Ray's interpretation in English and the original excerpts published in volume II and found that these two mss and the one currently presented in this volume - all begin with salutation to Gaṇeśa and all refer to Mahādeva and the disciple Śri Rāma. This clearly identifies the three Sûvarṇatantra / Svarṇatantra mss as works of the Śaiva Tantra genre of the medieval times.

The mss published by Ray included only two *kalpas*. These were almost word to word similar. However, the ms IM 5384, presented in this volume, shares similarity only in case of the first kalpa with these two. The second kalpa in the mss published by Ray is dissimilar to the second kalpa of the ms IM 5384, and the rest of the eight *kalpa*s in this ms are completely new. The most significant fact about the Sûvarṇatantra ms studied by us is that this is a text mostly focused on metallurgical practices, rather than the Ayurvedic aspect of *rasâyana* and that more than transmutation of gold the text refers to diverse processes of metallurgy involving different metals and mineral substances albeit in a manner illustrative of the poor pedagogy of the composer. All the clues related above and the chemical metallurgical information contained in this ms., especially when compared with the Ain i Akbari, convey the impression that this ms on suvarṇatantra is most probably a 16th century or later composition.

An interpretation of the information contained in this ms is attempted below. The main aim was to find some references to contemporary practices bordering in what is now generally regarded as stages of proto-chemistry. In fact scientific researches on medieval Indian metallurgy, ayurvedic pharmacy and other applications reveal the reality of such practices.

1. Tailakanda Kalpa

The text begins with reference to God Śiva, the Lord of medieval *Rasatantra* tradition. Śiva is invoked and the worshipper acknowledges that He had already imparted to the disciple the knowledge of *Rasâyanaparâ*, which is said to increase health and prosperity. Going by the text, it appears that the composer of the text makes lofty claims about being conversant with several different but related branches of *Rasavidyâ*. Apparently Śiva had enlightened the disciple on the subject of *Ratnatantra*. The disciple also claims to have learnt all about (preparation of) two thousand *guṭikâ* (5) and six hundred preparations of killed mercury, *dhâtunâm aṣṭakalpa* or the knowledge of (handling) eight metals, *dhâturyoga* – working with metals and *ratnânâm karaṇa* - making of minerals. The worshipper admits that Śiva had narrated about the seven hundred categories of *haritâla*. (6) The protagonist in this text is by his own admission a poor man, seeking the technique or magic of making gold. Svarṇatantra was quite obviously the chief goal of the invoker. The plea of poverty is made before the God to justify the desire for attaining knowledge about this magical technique.

The style of composition of the text is similar to the other two texts studied by Acharya P.C. Ray. The text is divided in ten *kalpas*, each named after a particular real or imagined ingredient of alchemical recipe. Often it appears that two ingredients have been combined.

The recipes are somewhat vague especially as far as measures or quantities of substances or even exact mechanism of procedure are concerned. But more than that, very often the information that is conveyed supposedly by Śiva to his disciple Rāma is worded in half or little – understood forms. Interpreting the scientific content of the information therefore is difficult and much of what has been gauged in this analysis of the text remains hypothetical. However, there are some very interesting and significant clues to contemporary knowledge of metals, minerals, botanical substances, pyrotechnology etc, which leaves us in wonderment and it is quite possible to correlate these information with those from other earlier *Rasaśāstra* texts which have more clarity. Not only that, some of the descriptions may be linked with medieval metallurgical practices as illuminated in the Ain i Akbari of Abul Fazl and some Chinese manuscripts. This current interpretation mainly keeps to the information from the manuscript and only refers to other sources where these are directly related to the interpretation of the present manuscript.

The manuscript actually touches upon alchemical techniques from the 12th line of the first *Kalpa*. Descriptions in this first *Kalpa* revolves round the ingredient- *tailakanda* (oily bulb). *Tailakanda* is described to be famous as *Siddhakanda*.

A physical description follows, that it is like the bulb of lotus - *kamalavatjñeya*. The identification is a matter of importance here. The leaves are described as *Kañjavabdhiśe/kañjavabhdhiśī*. The meaning is not clear but could be taken as - produced from water lotus or born from lotus. (7)

The thing is next referred as '*Tailakanda*' or oilbulb (7a), or oilybulb, or a bulb - like plant exuding oil. So the final description is that the plant is formed like a lotus, with leaves, sprouting like lotus and has an oil – bulb and is known as some kind of lotus. It is next mentioned that - "the large leaf always exudes oil" "*Tathaivatu mahâpattram tailam śravati sarvadâ*" . This *mahâpatra* - may also indicate the principal, central or largest leaf of the plant.

The tailakanda is therefore described as the oily bulb or a bulb plant exuding oil, which grows in water. It has the morphology similar to the lotus, if the composer's veracity is to be accepted. The leaves are described as sprouting like those of a lotus. The large leaf '*mahâpatram*', is said to always exude oil.

In the next two lines of the verse, it is stated that this "plant" always stays in water - (aquatic plant?) - "*jalamadhyam sadâputra vārjaiva / varjevaja pratitiṣthati.*" Although we get the term '*vārjaiva*' in the ms, the grammatically correct term is 'vārjevaja' which means 'born out of aqua plants'. (8) Incidentally '*vāryâmalaka*' is described as a variety of myrobalan growing near water . It is listed in the Monier Williams under the words formed of root 'var.' (9) So this kind of reference to water plants is not uncommon.

The plant is next described as a bulb reputed (*vikhyāt*) to be a '*viṣakanda*' - a poisonous bulb, (first Kalpa line 14) with the potency to kill twenty - eight persons. The significance is not in numbers but in the fact that the plant was generally known for its poisonous property. This great bulb is described as '*tailaśrāvī*'.

The gist of the descriptions is that it is an oil exuding bulb - a lotus – like plant, which is poisonous and that the oil it exudes spreads for ten cubits in water where it grows.

The next two lines are rather symbolic and perhaps bear a mark of superstition. The God warns his disciple that a snake lurks underneath the plant. Whether this was a common notion derived from frequent observation of aquatic snakes taking shelter beneath the lotus plant in ponds, we cannot be sure. It might contrarily have been an allusion to the dangers in the ways of collecting the *kanda*. (10)

The next lines in the text describe further what was to be done with this bulb - like plant.

A needle was to be used to prick the bulb and it is told that the needle would immediately get dissolved – '*sucī drāva ksanāt*'. The question is, what does this test with a needle imply? Was it meant that the insertion of the needle into the bulb results in exudation of a sap or resin - like fluid, which has a strong acidic property that can dissolve the metal needle? The discussion on the concept and actuality of *'drāva'* has been discussed below. Incidentally, the metallic composition of the needle is not specified. Iron needles were commonplace items, however, brass needles were not unknown at the time (11) and have been referred as used in this very text later on.

The question is - did the expert already know what to expect of the right species? In that case, the Suvarnatantra is talking about a rare but known species of aquatic plant. Now, considering the repetitions on its poisonous nature, the aquatic plant, like lotus or water lily nelumba or nymphaecae, which is not lotus and is poisonous (matches with Nymphaea odorata Ait ssp. Tuberosa) could possibly fit the bill. But there can be no certainty to it. This bulb is to be procured, rubbed with mercury three times in a mortar. The oil exuded by the plant leaf has also to be collected. This oil is to be poured into a crucible along with the paste of the *Kanda* and mercury. The next description is not very clear. However, the general indication is that the crucible is heated in a bamboo sticks fire– '*vaṁśāṅgāreṇa*'. The mercury is immediately "killed". This mercury if consumed is said to alleviate hunger and sleep. The mixture now (mercury is predominant in the concept) has the property to convert base metal, thousand times it own weight, into gold. This is in essence an allusion to the process of extracting pure mercury from cinnabar – which is supposed to transmute base metals into gold. (12)

The next preparation under the Tailakanda kalpa is as follows.

The same oil (extracted from the *siddhakanda / tailakanda*) is put in a mortar along with pure *haritāla* or orpiment which is broken into seven parts and rubbed everyday for twenty days. This *haritāla* takes time to be "killed". Here it is repeated that this preparation is done with recourse to heating. When the *haritāla,* thus prepared and heated, becomes smokeless, the preparation should be poured on the eight metals in their mother form (ore form) and is said to act as *'drāva'*. Thus there is a repeated reference to a solution that dissolves the eight metals. It is then proclaimed that if this mixture or *rasa* – as it is often referred to in the text - is poured on copper the copper turns into excellent gold (śloka 20-23). (13) It is also stated that if the oil and orpiment mixture is poured on tin and bell metal (*Kāńgsa*) it turns into silver. (14)

When copper, iron, brass (*rīti*) and silver (*tāra*) is thrown together with calamine (*kharpara*) and mercury (*sūta*) - the action immediately turns them into bright gold. (15)

Next, a task is set for the person pursuing the object. It is mentioned that an expert in this field would next collect together (*samānīya*) the thick part of this mercury *(udarasama pāradam)* (16) in shade and rub it for twenty one days in a mortar. The mercury is then to be put in what is termed a *'lohāyantra"* (an iron vessel or an iron furnace?) along with equal quantity of rasa. Now, here we have the appearance of a new element.

The mixture of rasa (?) and pārada in the same quantity is to be put in a dish (*sthāllouḥ).* A coin made of iron (*louha mudrā*) is next put in the dish in this solution. The coin is described as floating in the mixture (*tataścaret* - floating in mercury?). This coin, now called ghorā mudrā (17) is put into the mercury rasa solution in the iron vessel and a rite of yôga is to be performed at this moment (*yogakrameṇ?a* ca) and the vessel is put on the oven "*cullika"* with lots of care. (18)

The next lines describe the process of firing and the operation of the furnace. The description is neither clear nor available in details but the little that can be understood is that the pyrotechnology was complicated enough to merit mention. It is told that a *śańku*, which might have been a peg, nail or a gnomon, was inserted into the furnace (probably to hold the lohāyantram in proper place in the oven) and the next few words taken together, implies that the mercury (with the iron coin?) is killed thereby. This description might refer to the process of inserting the dish with the mercury and the iron coin into a prepared and already heated furnace.

The fire in the furnace is described as *dīpāgnim* - which burnt like *haṭāgnim* – shining very bright (*haṭ, haṭati* – to shine, bright) (19) The indication is that the fire was burning at a very high temperature. A few specific wood fuel are recommended for use in this process a few lines later. The woods of forest trees, *Vamśa:* bamboo - Bambusa vulgaris, and *khadira* tree – Acacia catechu, etc., which grow only a little every month – - *māsa mātra vyātīte tu kalāmātra prajāyate* (Kalā = a small portion) are pointed out as the best for the operation. (20)

The whole process of firing is to be conducted along with the initiating rites and purifying chanting (*Puraścaryāputa mantram*). There is also the advice delivered here that, prior to undertaking the task of firing, the practice of celibacy was to be followed by anyone who desired to achieve results from these instructions. There is a hint that the fire would gain high temperature only if one follows celibacy.

Observations of the incidents during the firing referred to here are difficult to understand and rationalize, but they are as follows: First, it is described, that the 'something'—probably referring to the heat,- flies first to the coin, which rises and gets purified (*dhruvam*). Then the mercury moves down with a sound. When the sound is heard a further ingredient whose name starts with 'ka...' (cannot be read) is to be added. This 'Ka ......' should be mixed with the mercury. The resultant purified mercury is not to be consumed. This purified ingredient would turn bell metal (*Kāṅgsa*), if mixed with yellow orpiment (*vaṅgari*) (21) as white as white - wash (*sudhākarah*?) every time it is used. A minute part of this purified mercury put to one part of base metals would purify them a thousand times – *Kalām̐ śoyamśa yukto hi śatavedhī bhaved dhruvam*". The śloka might also mean that - one part investment would bring a hundred portions. And for twelve months the process is prescribed to be continued.

Now if the whole operation is taking place in a closed furnace, the pyrotechnology and operations of metal and fire in the furnace would remain a mystery to anyone not experienced in the techniques of firing and metallurgy. The suggestion of chanting and rituals accompanying the actual procedure could have been posed as a psychological support during a process, the technique and working of which was little understood by the initiate alchemist. The sound in the furnace guides the practitioner of alchemy, otherwise a novice in matters of metallurgy, that the metal has been prepared.

The above process is said to fulfill all desires. The last line before the conclusion is difficult to read. However, there seems to be an indication that as if the blessing of that bulbous tree with only root is sought by the devotee. The tree therefore, is ascribed a magical significance. It is unfortunate that we cannot ascertain the exact species mentioned here based on the description provided.

The assumption could be made, that the first kalpa on *tailakanda* is actually describing in elaborate manner the contemporary process of extracting pure mercury followed by the alchemists who received great support from the metallurgists so that the alchemists themselves never handled and knew about the working process in their details. Or it may have been that while some of the alchemists in the medieval times were actually proficient in chemical – metallurgical processes, some self proclaimed alchemists knew little about the actual chemical processing - if we go by the evidence of the ms discussed here.

Firstly, one may refer to the process of *banwāri*, and the process of extracting gold form salôni or slag left after refining gold by the use of mercury. These have already been discussed in the chapter on the "Origin of Rasāyana".

2. Kaṭukuṣmâṇḍa Kalpa.

Kaṭukuṣmāṇḍa would be a species of bitter gourd, if taken literally. The description of its use indicates that *Kaṭukuṣmāṇḍa* was either metaphoric or having a different connotation altogether. *Kuṣmāṇdi* is identified as the plant species: Benincasa Cerifera Savi by Mira Roy and B.V. Subbarayappa. They have also listed the chemical properties of this species, which are as the following: it contains fixed oil, starch, an alkaline cucurbitine, acid resin, proteids, myosin, vitellin, sugar, vitamin B, etc. (22) The Kaṭu Kuṣmāṇḍa has not been specifically identified either by Roy and Subbarayappa or in the Monier Williams dictionary. However, it might be a bitter variety of vegetable marrow with different chemical properties. *Kaṭu* is generally described in Ayurvedic texts as a particular characteristic or property (guna) or rasa. The Suśruta described it as bitter and caustic, strong, smelling, pungent and acerbic- all qualities of alkali or salt. Monier Williams describes the term "*Kaṭucaturjātaka*" as "an aggregate of four acid substances" – namely a) cardamoms, b) bark and c) leaves of Laurus Cassia and d) black pepper. P.K. Gode (23) identified *pattraka* as Laurus Cassia (24) However, most probably none of these have been indicated as Kaṭukuṣmāṇḍa here.

Now the text goes on to describe that the juice of *Kaṭukuṣmâṇḍa* is to be extracted first.

This rasa poured on tin would transform it into silver. The description of tin, getting instantly transformed into silver if this juice

PLATE I ABRUS PRECATORIUS

PLATE II ACHYRANTHES ASPERA

PLATE III ALHAGI MAURORUM

PLATE IV ARDISIA HUMILIS

PLATE V AVERRHOA CARAMBOLA

PLATE VI BENINCASA CERIFERA

PLATE VII BENINCASA HISPIDA

PLATE VIII BOERHAVIA DIFFUSA

PLATE IX BOMBAX CEIBA MALABARICUM

PLATE X CALOTROPIS GIGANTEA

PLATE XI CLITORIA TERNATEA L.

PLATE XII CURCULIGO ORCHOIDES

PLATE XIII CURCUMA LONGA

PLATE XIV ELETTERIA CARDAMOMUM

PLATE XV FERULA GALBANIFLUA*

PLATE XVI FICUS OPPOSITIFOLIA

PLATE XVII GOSSYPIUM INDICUS

PLATE XVIII INULA RACEMOSA

PLATE XIX LAGENARIA VULGARIS

PLATE XX MORINGA OLEIFERA

PLATE XXI PHYLLANTHUS ACIDUS

PLATE XXII PUNICA GRANATUM

PLATE XXIII RICINUS COMMUNIS

PLATE XXIV SOLANUM INDICUM

PLATE XXV TRIBULUS TERRESTRIS

is poured on it might have been a reference to three possible alternates. First, the most common metallurgy concerning silver is the process of extraction of silver from a lead ore, which generally contains some amount of silver, a process practiced by the metal smiths in the contemporary mints. In this case one has to assume that lead was confused with tin. The process of extracting silver from lead, commonly known to the metallurgists since long was probably outside the ken of the alchemist in the *Sūvarṇatantra* and hence the confusion. (25)

The other option is that the reference in these lines is directed to the incidence of the creation of a silver – tin alloy. (26) This process would require the deliberate addition of some amount of silver with tin and might have required the use of an organic acid. The acid in question therefore is derived from plants, probably known in its natural form to the actual experimenter but unknown to the composer of the " Sūvarṇatantra".

The third alternative was that the lines were truthfully sticking to the belief of transmuting tin into silver and not describing alloying.

There is an interesting reference to the tradition of transmuting tin into silver in India in the Theosophist Captain Olcott's Diary, (27) which indicates that the tradition was continuing down to the late nineteenth century. Incidentally Olcott's encounter with the alchemy enthusiast also involved the use of a coin to oxidize the metal and extract the pure metal from it. This probably matches the information contained in the last part of the "Tailakanda Kalpa". So far as the actual concept of transmutation among the ancient alchemists is concerned it had a lot to do with the practical advancements made in the workrooms of the ceramic manufacturers and the metallurgists. Transmutation is the act of changing a substance, tangible or intangible, from one form or state into another. To the alchemists of old, this meant the conversion of one physical substance into another, particularly base metals such as lead into valuable silver and gold. To the modern scientists, this means the transformation of one element into another by one or a series of nuclear decays or reactions. Although people worked with gold, silver, copper, iron, tin, lead, carbon, sulfur, and mercury in ancient times, they had little understanding of chemistry and could write little about it. At this time chemistry was an art, not a science. The alchemists attempted to develop schemes to transmute base metals into gold and silver through various chemical manipulations of mixtures and distillations. The alchemists were spurred on by what appeared to be some success, for example, in the production of very small amounts of gold from lead ore by their chemical procedures. This gold was undoubtedly present in trace amounts in the original ores and was not produced by transmutation. The same applies for transmutation of tin or lead into silver. (28) Interestingly enough, the "Codex Atlanticus" of Leonardo da Vinci contains a reference to separating gold from silver by using a mineral solvent. (29) This fifteenth century reference has a long Asian background which we shall refer to in the following pages, which will also indicate the possibilities mentioned above.

To continue with the descriptions and prescriptions in the manuscript: the reference to transmutation or rather alloying processes involving the use of minerals and botanical acids and alkalis is continued with reference to other baser metals.

The same juice (juice of *Kaṭukuṣmāṇḍa*) poured on copper (*tāmra*), iron (*lôha*), brass (*rīti*) and borax *(taṅkaṇa)* mixed together (*tāmre lohe tathā rītyām ṭaṅkaṇa tadgal ṭadrasamksipet*) is sáid to yield a flow of gold, which appears like *jāmbunada. Jambunada*, not *Jāmbunada*, - is the river of fables flowing from the mount Meru. (30) This is a direct reference to transmutation of base metals to gold. However, the concept of combining many metals together to obtain a transformed and new metal is also clear in this reference.

Next is the reference to seven metals (*saptadhātu*) (31). This particular *śloka* of the Suvarṇatantra describes that if *saptadhātu* along with silver (*tāra*) - was rubbed with this rasa (juice of '*Kaṭukuṣmānda*') again and again in a mortar, a flow will appear and the encrustations (*kalaṅkastu bhavet śuddha śatavedhī bhavet dhruvam*) on the metals will be cleansed and they (pieces of the metals thus polished) would appear to be a hundred fold of their earlier properties. This is a reference purely to a process of chemical polishing, in which the chemical agent is extracted from the plant mentioned above.

3. Raktavîjakaṭu Kalpa

The next section deals with *Raktavîja* preparations, which is said to bring *'ṛddhibala'*- or power of wealth - a process follows which is said to be yielding gold.

Raktavîja has been defined in Monier Williams, dictionary as the pomegranate tree (32) The nomenclature here may pertain to a bitter variety of pomegranate. '*Kaṭu*' – generally denotes alkaline substances or the astringent taste – *kaṭu rasa*. This *Kaṭu Raktavîja* is to be collected as it provides '*ṛddhibala*' – with extensive power and probably, it is also implied that the extract from this fruit is said to increase the power of *rasa*, which might or might not have been mercury. The first process indicates that already purified copper was to be treated with this '*rasa*' – which was probably strengthened by addition of the extract from *Kaṭu Raktavîja*, which turns the copper into the pure '*Gâñgeya*' gold. (33) Interestingly enough, while 'rasa' generally denotes mercury in alchemical texts, this description, if right in its pronouncements of results, would make it wrong if we identify *rasa* in this particular preparation as mercury. The transmuted copper, which turned into '*Gâñgeya*', - most likely refers to brass, and in that case, '*rasa*' or rather '*rasaka*' here is the extract from calamine ore - that is zinc extract. (34)

The next line is difficult to read and comprehend due to the condition of the manuscript. It reads something like:

'jale/jalani vaṅsyekṛtyâdou rasam tatra vinikṣipet'

However the word is probably '*vangsya*' and therefore refers to '*vaṅg*' or tin. Śiva (the teacher) advises Rāma (the devotee) to put tin into water and pour the '*rasa*' into it. The tin is said to turn into silver immediately and obtain the colour of '*kundapuṣpa*'. The colour of the transmuted tin is said to be like a golden - white flower or jasmine, which is the normal colour of a white metal with a large percentage of tin and a part of *rasaka* or zinc.

The next lines claim that half a *rati* (1/8th of a *mâsa*) of this silver, if thrown into any metal would to turn into active "*Rakśmivedhî*" or rather "*rakṣmivedhî*. This recipe is clearly different from the earlier two, in its expected result. The meaning of the term '*rakṣmivedhî*' becomes important. One of the definitions of *Rakṣa* in Monier Williams Dictionary (35) is described as ashes used as a preservative, possibly in amulets as a part of belief system. *Rakṣa* is therefore anything protective – shield – like. '*Vedh*', as a verb or noun is the action of penetration or piercing and as noun it is that substance which pierces. A meaning closer to the *Rasatantra* practices would be the definition (36): "mixture of fluids" to which quicksilver is subjected". In the conceptual world of the alchemists '*vedhana*' meant the transmutation act and '*vedhîn*' is the substance that transmutes metals. (37) Among many other definitions – these two are closer to our subject. Is this then a direct reference to the chemical process of making a substance that can pierce or rather, dissolve any metal? Or an indirect reference to the process of dissolving metals with the use of a solution? Now it is known that the solution *aqua regia* is generally used to dissolve gold and silver and that it is a highly corrosive, fuming yellow or red solution. The mixture is formed by freshly mixing concentrated nitric acid and concentrated hydrochloric acid, usually in a volumetric ratio of one to three respectively. It is one of the few reagents that dissolves gold and platinum.

There is a detailed discussion in P.C. Ray on the knowledge of mineral acids in medieval India, which actually clarifies the fact that some specific mineral acids were in the making in South Asia and the Arab world, especially from the 13th century onwards. The Sanskrit medical works of the 16th – 17th centuries like the "Rasakaumudī" of Mādhava, "Rasaratnapradīpa" and Bhaiṣajyaratnāvalī of Govindadāsa, clearly refer to a *mahâdrâvakarasa* – a powerful liquid solvent. (38) *Śañkhadrâvaka* is mentioned in the two "Suvarṇataṇtra" mss discussed by P.C. Ray. (39) It is mentioned in these two mss that "*Śañkhadrâvaka*" solvent along with mercury is to be placed in a glazed crucible (refractory material) and subjected to heat. Mercury is regarded as 'killed by this process and then it is claimed that this 'killed' mercury could convert the eight metals into gold.

"*Śānkhadrāvasya bhedān hi tatkalpan sṛṇu sāmpratam*
Louhadrāvastathā tāmradrāvaścaiva dvitīyaka
Śānkhadrāvastṛtīyah? syāt hantālaśca caturthaka
Dantadrāvaḥ pañcama syāt amlavedhī tu madhyamah? ."

The idea that such a powerful solvent would transmute all base metals into gold was floating in the world of alchemy from Arabia to China. There is a claim that the important mineral acids like nitric acid, sulfuric acid, and hydrochloric acid, were all first produced by the Arabs. These have remained some of the most common products in the chemical industry for over a thousand years. (40) Potassium nitrate (saltpetre) was known under various names to the Arabs in an early time as it was known to Khalid ibn Yazid (Calid) (Khalid ibn Yazid ibn Mu'awiya (dt. 635-704 CE to 709) (41) it is used as a flux in metallurgical operations and for producing nitric acid and aqua regia. Recipes for these uses are found in the works of Jabir ibn Hayyan (42), popularized by Europeans as Geber, (dt. 815), Abu Bakr al-Razi (dt. 925) (43); and other Arabic alchemists. (44). In fact acids and salts of various types from different natural sources were being made as early as the days of the Suśruta. *Yavakṣāra,* the ashes of the barley plant or the impure carbonate of potash, sauvarcala or saltpetre, sarjikâ or natron – have all been described as ingredients in the Suśruta. The term '*drâvaka*' has also been coined in the Rasaśâstra texts from the 16th – 17th centuries, implying the use of mineral acids much before that time. In fact, the Rasârnava of the 11th century had clearly referred to a recipe for mineral solvent. But this material was formed into a '*viḍa*' or pill and not as a liquid. The recipe is as follows: *Kâsîsam* (green vitriol), *saindhava* rock salt' *kâñcî* - the pyrites, *sauvîram* (stibnite), *vyoso*- the aggregate of 3 spices, *gandhakam* - sulphur, *sauvarcalam* - salt petre, *sarjikâ* – natron, *mâlatinîrasambhavam* - the juice of pressed *mâlati*, - all moistened with the juice of the root of śigru - *Moringa pter.*, makes a '*viḍa'* which would kill all metals, (45) The use of the urine of cow, the plant *eraṇḍa* - ricinus communis and *kadalî* - banana - Musa sapientum - burnt into ashes - have also been repeatedly referred in the Āyūrvedic compendiums as well as the early Rasa Śâstra texts. (46) Sal ammoniac is termed as '*narasâra*'. (47) or '*navasâra*' (48) In fact, the Rasaratnasamuccaya (49) describes that '*navasâra*' is obtained from the decomposed shoots of bamboo and the wood of Careya arborea. It is produced during the burning of the brick in a hearth. That is why the other name of '*navasâra*' is '*culikâlavaṇa*'. It is supposed to kill mercury, liquefy iron, act as a stomachic, said to absorb spleen and aid in digestion – all in different measures of intake or use. However, it is also mentioned by P.C. Ray that the term *navasâra* originates from the Persian – *nausâdâr*. Royle has already pointed out that the Sanskrit Rasaśâstra tradition must have been familiar with the process of extraction of Sal Ammoniac from bricks or mud ovens made of soil containing animal excreta, which must have yielded the salt as a by - product on heating in hearths. (50) Thus what it all purports is the assimilation of knowledge from all sources leading to new discoveries and innovations in the field of practical proto – chemistry, if we care to look behind the façade of alchemy.

But the documentation of making of *aqua regia* was done in Arabic alchemy first. Mixing a vitriol with nitre (potassium nitrate) and heating produced vapours - which gave nitric acid. Commonly known as nitre (51) potassium nitrate, KNO_3, is a mineral found on and just under the ground in desert regions. Nitre occurs in Bihar, India, Iran, and Cape Province, South Africa. Purification of potassium nitrate was also mastered by the Arabs before the 11th century. There are two celebrated works which described the purification processes: one is by Ibn Bakhtawayh in his book al-Muqaddimat (dt. 1029) (52) and the other is by the Arab chemist and engineer Hassan al-Rammah of Syria in his book al-Furusiyya wa al-Manasib al-Harbiyya (dt. 1270) (53) The first complete purification process for potassium nitrate was described by al-Rammah, who first described the use of potassium carbonate (in the form of wood ashes) to remove calcium and magnesium salts from the potassium nitrate. (54) Adding sal ammoniac (ammonium chloride) to nitric acid gave *aqua regia*, so named for its ability to dissolve gold. Hydrochloric acid ("spirit(s) of salt" - a name still used in commerce/pharmacy as late as the early 1970s) was also known to the Middle Ages; certainly it was known to Paracelsus (early 1500s). The word alkaline comes from the Arabic *al-qily*, which means "to roast in a pan" or "the calcinated ashes of plants". By leaching the ashes with water, one can obtain a solution of sodium or potassium carbonate (to use the modern terms). This is then mixed with slaked lime (calcium hydroxide) and you get a solution of NaOH or KOH. This technique was described in writing in the 1900s, but may have existed for many years prior. The descriptions in Suśruta already discussed in the Introductory Chapter throw sufficient light on the fact that such techniques were also employed to similar ends by the Āyūrveda practitioners and later by the *Rasa Śāstra* experts. That is why the common use of *aqua fortis* with reference to a vernacular name '*ashkara*' (mispronounced from *kṣāra*?) has been mentioned in *the Ain – i- Akbari, i*n connection with purification of silver. The indication to a metal solvent is found once more in the ninth Kalpa in this manuscript. Thus we may fairly accept that a reference to a solvent is implied here too.

This is followed by the description of the testing. Needles made of each of the base metals mentioned should be put into this solvent and it was declared that they would either immediately or with time be found to have dissolved. (55) Here we may cite the examples of chemical and metallurgical processes found in the Air i Akbari and other texts for comparison. We may begin by citing the process of banwāri, a gold alloy, and then to the process of extracting gold from salôni or slag, left after refining gold, by the use of mercury. These have already been discussed in the introductory chapter. Now, in this chapter we may go into a more detailed discussion on the medieval Indian Knowledge of acids, alkalies and solvents. There is a clear reference to the use of '*rāsī*' or aqua fortis in the Ain I Akbari for the refinement of silver which was mentioned by Abul Fazl to be composed of saltpetre and 'ashkara'. (56) Saltpetre was known as '*Sauvarcala*' and there is a clear reference to the composition of "*agnicūrṇa*" with *sauvarcala* (saltpetre, natron), *gandhaka* (sulphur), *arka* (Calotropis Gigantea) and *sudhā* (lime) in the Śukrānīti. However, this portion was probably a later interpolation added in the medieval period after the fourteenth century when the use of gun powder had become known in India. (57) Now, *suvaracala* was used as a plant source for *kṣāra* or salt since the days of the Caraka Samhitā, but it was probably confused with the earth salt of potassim nitrate in the early days before the use for gun powder, which was a much later incident. P.C. Ray points out that *sauvarcala* (obtained from *suvarcala* plant) was identified as salt petre in the earlier Sanskrit traditions, while it was identified as a source of natron in the later texts. (58) Our discussions made above on the advancements in Arabic alchemy clarifies how the knowledge of acids became clear with time - that is to say that the knowledge of the mineral acids grew with contributions from alchemical practices all over the world – the 'international world of Chimie or *Rasavidya'*, Arab, Chinese and Indian. Jewelry professionals points out that *aqua regia* dissolves both platinum and gold.(59) Nitric acid however absorbs silver and nickel. (60) Experts also confirm the use of nitric acid in testing on silver. Nitric acid is extracted from natural sources while searching for possible plants that were used for preparing mineral solvents some tested references caught attention. One example has been discussed below, and, although it is in no way connected to the medieval Indian scene, it throws light on why and how use of plants in Indian tradition of alchemy might have been effective. One botanical source is available from Bolivia, which has been tested in recent times. The results of the test is as given below.

Coto (*Synonym.*—Paracoto Bark) (61) is a bark of unknown botanical source, derived from a large tree, probably belonging to a species of *Cryptocarya* /Laurineae/ *Aniba coto*. It is obtained from Bolivia. The bark occurs in flat or slightly curved heavy pieces, up to about 60 centimetres long, 6 centimetres broad, and 8 to 14 millimetres thick.

Constituents.—The chief constituent of coto (paracoto) bark is paracotoin (dioxymethylene-phenylcumalin), a crystalline bitter principle, which gives a yellow colour with nitric acid; other constituents are leucotin, hydrocotoin (benzoyl-phloroglucinol dimethyl ether), methyl hydrocotoin, protocotoin, methyl protocotoin (oxy-leucotin), and piperonylic acid. So-called true coto bark contains cotoin (benzoyl-phloroglucinol methyl ether), a crystalline powder, which yields a red colour with nitric acid, and leucotin (phenylcumalin). Both barks also contain a little volatile oil, resin, and tannin. (62)

Indian plants as counterparts of this might be Niter bush (Bot.), a genus (Nitraria) of thorny shrubs bearing edible berries, and growing in the saline plains of Asia and Northern Africa. Other possible botanical sources for different alkali and salts might be – Salsola, (63) Calotropis Gigantea, Kanṭakāri (64), Inula Racemosa or Puskarmul (65) and Ferula Galbaniflua. (66) The description in this Kalpa therefore is not a lone item. There was a growing body of knowledge regarding the chemical properties in application of natural substances. Our manuscript reveals a half baked reception of such knowledge floating in the contemporary world.

4. Katutumba Kalpa

Next section is named after "*Kaṭutumbī*" – which is clearly defined in Monier Williams dictionary as "a kind of bitter gourd" (67) while Mira Roy and B.V. Subbarayappa identify it clearly as the wild variety of *Lagenaria vulgaris* Seringe - but the spelling is "*Kaṭutumbī*". Śiva advices that the *Kaṭutumbī* variety, especially if it bore bitter seeds, was to be cut open carefully. Needles of brass are mentioned next (*Pittalānam*) (68) which are used in the operation. The needles are to be used in piercing the fruit several times in the month of *Kārtika*- an autumnal month. (November, in all likelihood). This probably covers the idea that hile the *Kaṭutumbi* gourd may be plucked before, it should be kept aside for some time till autumn appeared. In fact, the next lines clarify this process. It is prescribed that the fruits should be watched even till the month of *Māgha* (*Mārgaśīrṣa* - January). If the seeds are pierced before that, the fruit will be destroyed. Even so, the fruits that get rotten should be discarded. Finally (in *Māgha* probably) the needles steeped in rasa should be inserted in the seeds, and kept that way for a month. Finally these needles should be placed over an earthenware dish and heated on fire of forest timbers and "*vanôpala*" – *vana upala*- forest stone-fires (charcoal?). On being heated the needles were predicted to turn into gold. The needles than are to be kept carefully covered between two earthen - ware dishes. This gold again turns the colour of *jambunada* on being put over bamboo fire and by applying forest stones (?) (69)

An alternative is also provided for the method of firing the 'rasa' - steeped' brass needles, whereby, the needles are to be placed in the '*Mūṣā*' or '*Mūṣikā*' or crucible and then the crucible having been put on fire-embers helps create the metallic 'transmutation' – '*tatradhmātou.*(69a) First the '*kāñcana*' or 'golden metal' turns '*divya*' – or bright and molten and then ends up as solid gold.

Now this is very clearly an adaptation from the working knowledge of the metal smiths, especially either or both of the gold jeweler and the coin mint workers. The description in the Ain-i-Akbari clearly refers to the manufacture of brass needles for testing gold standards. The brass needles were tipped with gold dots of various degrees of purity (a mixture of ban and pure gold, the ratio of which varied for different gradations of gold). Now this process involved soldering. The exact details of manufacturing of these gold-tipped needles are not available from the Ain. (70)

However, the reference, a sixteenth century one, could be related with how the composer of the *Sūvarṇatantra* came to possess the convoluted idea of brass needles turning into gold. It is possible that a kind of plant extract was used in facilitating the soldering. The whole idea of these brass needles tipped with gold might have been internalized in a jumbled up manner by the contemporary aspirants of gold – the quick alchemist.

5. Tumbîsiddhidâ or Siddhatumbi Kalpa

The next chapter is dealing with what the composer of the Suvarṇatantra calls "*Siddhatumbī*" - a plant, which gives success. The alchemy in this particular *kalpa* indicates the use of a number of plants for the first time in the ms. It is suggested that purified '*Vańga*' or tin is to be put into a crucible. *Śvetā* and *Girikarṇi* along with *Yoṇivallī* (all names of plants) are taken together and the juice extracted from them is poured into the crucible. Put on fire, the tin turns into the colour of '*kunda*' flowers within the crucible. *Girikarṇi* is defined as the botanical species – Alhagi Maurorum L. (71) A very surprising input of information comes from the Monier Williams Dictionary regarding the possible meaning of the term '*yôṇi*' in connection with alchemy. The Dictionary provides (72) as an alternative definition of "*Yonī*" – a part of fire pit, or heat or a mine or copper. In the case of the last two definitions it is suggested that such uses for the term have been found in Sanskrit texts but they have not been included in any previous published Dictionary. *Vallī* is the general term for 'creeper' (73). However, '*vallī*' is also defined as a 'class of medicinal plants' – *'vallī pañcamūla'* including *vidarī, sārivā, rajani* and *ajā śṛṅgī*, etc. (74) Incidentally, a term - 'tāmra vallī' has also been listed under the definition for the term 'Tālaka' in the Monier Williams Dictionary p. 445 , which refers to a plant - Curculigo orchoides L. (75). Since one connotation of the term '*yonī*' refers to copper the joint term '*yonivallī*' might refer to '*tāmravallī*'.

The definitions of śvetā , which tallies with the discussions in the Suvarunatantra are listed below (76)

a) A small white shell or cowry.

b) Names of various plants, in different texts not recorded in published dictionaries.

c) The birch tree.

d) A white bignonia – *Boerhavia Procumbens* Roxb, or *Boerhavia diffusa R. - Punarnava* (77) In describing the patented *Punarnava* (US Patent 20030175373)– the description of the constituents of Boerhavia are said to include large quantities of potassium nitrate alkaloid. Mira Roy and BV Subbarayappa, identify the plant as an associated plant with *Girikarṇikā* and gives its popular name as white *Aparājitā*. (78) Lastly, the plant species:

e) Chyranthes Atropurpurea – this is a connotation derived from Susruta Samhita and Brhatsamhita (79)

Now the assumption would be that tin and various plants extracts, along or not with shell powder and copper thrown together in a crucible, turns the tin into a golden colour- the colour of the *Kunda* flower. This probably reflects the vague idea of obtaining another tin alloy – whitish in colour. '*Kunda*' is defined as a) a kind of jasmine- *jasminum multiflorum* or *pubescens*, or b) fragrant oleander- *Nerium odorum*, or c) the resin of the plant *Boswellia thurifera* (80) The colour indicated is therefore whitish yellow, which, however, matches with brass. Now, this might therefore probably indicate a mixed alloy with copper, tin and other catalysts, which bears a whitish colour. The other possibility is of course that antimony, which was often confused with tin, was used. It should be noted that there is no actual reference to the use of *'tumbi'* in this section.

Incidentally, several rasāyana preparations from lead and calx of brass or copper sulphate have been indicated in the Amarakoṣa and Suśruta. Calamine is referred to as *rasaka* (81) and *rasagarbha* is mentioned as collyrium prepared from calx of brass in the Amarakoṣa. (82) *Rasāñjana* (83) is another variety of collyrium made from vitriol of copper and Curcuma longa or from calx of brass with Amomum Anthorhizza or lastly from lead ore. *Sauvira* is also defined as antimony (84) *Kapôtāñjana* is described as the ore of antimony (85). So antimony - both as a trace elements in lead - and as an ore, was being used by the metallurgists and pharmacologists (preparing collyrium, etc.) since early historical times. Hence, it is a possibility that this whole process is actually a vague reference to copper-antimony or copper –calamine alloying which was mistaken for gold.

6. Śvetagokṣura Kalpa

The sixth section discusses the preparations from another plant variety: *śvetagokṣura,* which is described in the Ms to be famous among the knowledgeable as the supreme medicine. The recipe is very simple. Tin is to be purified with a lot of care and *gokṣura* dust thrown on the ore and the latter is then to be roasted "*pradhamet*" – the metallurgical process is clearly referred here.

The result is declared in the following words: "*Vańgastārutva tām tyajet*". If the words are singled out, the line may read thus: "*vańga* (*s*) *tāruttva tām tyājet.*" Either this refers to the separation of silver from tin: "*vańgas tāra ut tva tām tyājet*"; or, it may mean that the tin is enhanced in quantity and nobleness if the term is read as "*urutva*" or "*urusattva*".

'*Urutva*' – is defined as – "vastness, magnitude or excellent- the last meaning is used in the Ṛg and Atharva Veda Saṁhitas. (86) It might be taken to imply that the tin increases in quantity as a result. The term '*Urusattva*' on the other hand implies "noble nature" (87) and "*Urusa*" means producing abundantly. (88).

Now we have to find out whether *gokṣura* plant extract (*rasa*) contained an acid, which enriched the trace elements of zinc and nickel naturally present in a tin ore so that after being treated with the plant juice the tin appeared to be bright and white.

Gokṣura plant is defined as Tribulus terrestris L. (89) In fact Suśruta mentions *gokṣura dugdha* of the plant, which obviously refers to the medicinal use of the sap or extract. It is also mentioned in the Bṛhat Saṁhitâ (90)

Śvetā- may not be a term defining a specific species of *gokṣura*, but may actually refer to another ingredient- to be used along with *gokṣura*. *Śvetā* - could be 'a small white shell' as already mentioned above (91) in which case this may be close to the recipe of 'Śankhadrāvaka' - which is mentioned also in other alchemy texts. A notice of a united States Patent referring to use of shell Powder for silver polishing in 1905 is available.

Probably the tradition began much earlier and in the wider world of medieval alchemy. (The reference for the US Patent is provided below in end note 101. Vide discussions on 'śankhadrāvaka' 'aqua regia' 'aqua fortis' above. Also see endnote, 101.) If this identification is accepted here then the process that has been described in this section should be taken to refer to the separation of silver from tin ore.

7. Śveta eraṇḍa kalpa

The seventh section deals with *śveta eranḍa* (*eranḍa* is Ricinus Communis)

The passage gives the instruction that the oil of śveta *eranda* is to be extracted when the sun is in the Puṣyā constellation. This oil is to be rubbed with *karpūra* – camphor – extract from the tree species Camphora. The ointment thus prepared is meant for anointing both the eyes – añjana. It is claimed that this collyrium enabled one to visualize the seven netherworlds or 'pātāla' and is called the siddhāñjana used for success in *yôga*. The next recipe described is not very clear, but the śloka may be read in the following way: the root of this plant (*tanmūla)* is to be mixed along with what is termed as '*mārga pāṣāṇa'*, probably referring to bitumen or *śilājātu* (mārgapāsānam). However, the term 'pāṣāṇa' has been used in conjunction with different minerals, like 'gandhaka pāṣāṇa' and 'kānta - pāṣāṇa'. Generally 'pāṣāṇa' has been identified by Mira Roy and B.V. Subbarayappa, (New Delhi, 1993, Glossary, 133), as magnetic oxide of iron. This mixture is further mixed with *sūta* or mercury and the plant *kustha* (Saussurea lappa) and *Puṣkarmula* (Inula racemosa Hook).(92) f. – both plants suggested as used for their alkali or salt extract and, therefore, as a *drāva* and rubbed together in a crucible and kept shut.

The most plausible reading of the description seems to suggest that the *siddhāñjana* mixed with pure mercury, magnetic oxide of iron (?), Puṣkarmūla and the juice of *kustha* root and stalk should be poured into a crucible along with tin and heated on the fire of *śālmolī* (silk cotton tree) and *khadira* (catechu) woods thrice. That process is said to yield purified tin. This is extremely interesting since *siddhāñjana,* literally described as a magical eye ointment (93), is generally a composition containing antimony or lead with the beneficial properties of camphor (extract from bark of Cinnamomum Camphora), which purified the ointment and *eraṇḍa* oil used as a lubricant was meant probably as the base for the preparation of the eye ointment. Thus lead or antimony were one of the ingredients mixed with mercury and the chemical processing with this mixture on tin with *eraṇḍa* oil or castor oil and camphor would result in some kind of refining or polishing.

The mixture refined by repeated heating on wood fire (fire of Bombax Malabaricum, B. ceiba or silk cotton tree and Acacia catechu were specified) would yield an alloy that will be remarkably whitish-silvery. The production is described in the lines: "*tatvaṅgeṣu drutou kṣipram sahasrāṁśo vedhakam*" - the tin (*vaṅga*) is thus transmuted (*vedhakam*) very quickly.

The meaning of the next lines is not very clear to us. The lines describe the seeds of the plant. The seeds at the core of the flowers are described as white in colour. The outer seeds as well as the flowers and fruits of the plant are described as red in colour. This description is quite specific, and is probably provided for facilitating the identification of the plant. In fact there might be a hint contained here that it is the white seeds, which are to be used. At the end of this chapter, the name of the section is given as Śvetarakta Kalpa instead of śveta earṇḍa kalpa. Our identification reveals that *eraṇḍa* or Ricinus Communis does bear both whitish and red berries or dendrils.

8. Kākari Kalpa

The next section is a chapter on '*Kākarī*'.

Surprisingly enough the manuscript of "Sûvarṇa Tantra" under scrutiny contains only this particular section dealing specifically on āyurvedic '*Rasāyana*'. The rest are mostly devoted to the discussions on the alchemy of metals.

At the outset, the essential ingredient is described. It is clearly stated at the beginning that the meaning of the words – '*kāka*' and '*kākari*' is one and the same. The beautiful and fully ripe fruit of *kāka* is to be handpicked at a precise and astronomical time – when the sun is in the Ṛisya constellation. Monier Williams Dictionary gives one definition of '*kāka*' as the plant — Árdisia humilis. Moreover, the plants : a) *Kākoli*, b) Abrus Precatorius Taub., c) Ficus oppositifolia, d) Solanum indicum and e) *Raktikā* – are all listed under '*kāka*'.(93a) Raktikā is identified with Ardisia humilis. However, it is difficult for us to specify any one particular species among these which is meant for use in this particular section.

The juice of this fruit is to be rubbed with great pressure with mercury in a mortar for a day and that would kill the mercury. If the juice and (*vaddha*) killed mercury is mixed (*melayet*) for twenty days, it is said to yield a liquid or mercury mixture (sammelatâ) which, according to the opinion of experts, is denoted in the manuscript as '*guṭiṣaṣthî mukhâ*'. The word is not listed in the Monier Williams Dictionary. In all probability, it might be a 16th century term (technical in nature?). This mercury is clearly regarded as "*ṣaṣthisiddhśvara*" according to the traditions of the times.(93b)

The next step in this section instructs on a further 'rubbing' of this mercury with the juice of five parts (*pañcânga)* of the (same) plant. Finally this mercury is to be put in a crucible along with more juice from the plant and kept aside for a *prahara*. This process is said to 'kill' or refine the mercury. A *rattikâ* (1/8th of a masa in weight) of this mercury fed to a person regularly – with care, renders the man immortal (*cîrañjîvî*)– and ever young and charming, free of wrinkles and white hair (*balîpalitonirmukto Kâmarûpî*), if a specific amount – (*prasyasahasrasaṁbhakṣòî*) is consumed . The language of manuscript often reveals grammatical errors and spelling mistakes – probably committed in the process of copying down. The term '*prasya*' might actually stand for '*prasate'* (94) and has been used here to denote a 'desirable' quantity. The original *rattikâ* of prepared mercury would then be the 'mother tincture'.

Furthermore, the third stage is described. The above plant juice is to be placed in '*haritâla*' or orpiment and rubbed in a mortar for 8 *yâmas* (95). That makes it 8 x 3 = 24 hours. After that time the mixture becomes smokeless '*nirdhûma bhavati dhruvam'*. Intake of half a *rati* (1/6 th of a *mâṣa)* of this ingredient acts similar to a composition with mercury in it. (a poor man's substitute?) However, it is mentioned next that this prepared mercury mixed with gold makes a hundred thousand times the quality the gold had earlier. The composition with *tâlaka* is certified as having an enhancement to the degree of one hundred times (of its own unrefined and unmixed quality?) its own quality.

In the next lines we return once more to the processes of metallurgy. The juice of the leaves of this plant (*Kākari*), it is told, if thrown on tin – transmutes tin into '*tāra*' or silver – (96) of the colour of the *kunda* flowers. *Kunda* has already been discussed above. Very interestingly the term '*tārakṛt*' or 'silver - refiner is defined (97) as - lead. Does this process refer to the cupellation of silver from lead instead of transmutation of tin into silver? The question remains open as there is ground for us to believe that very often the term distinction between lead and tin was not clearly referred in medieval times. The next process is to do with the reaction of this mercury mixture with copper. It is prescribed that the juice of the fruits of that plant mixed with (mercury and) copper and "drāva"- a metal solvent (mineral acid to dissolve metals) turns it into pure '*jāmbunadam*' gold. (For explanation of *jāmbunada* – see above). Once more, copper as gold is implying brass or bronze.

The correct identification of the plant in question is important if the full implication of the pronouncements in this section is to be assessed. From the description it appears to be that possibly the species Abrus Precatorius Taub would be the correct identification. However it may be, one may at the least, safely comment on the nature of the discussions contained in this section on '*kākari*' to address the complete connotation of Indian tradition of Rasaśāstra or alchemy. This is the only section which refers to concoctions/ decoctions addressing both the purposes of alchemy- a) transmutation of base metals to gold and b) the chimeras of 'immortality' and 'ever - youth'.

9. Siddhasvarṇakalpa

The ninth section of the manuscript is highly interesting for a study of the 'mythical' concepts floating at the time centred round the practices of alchemy. This section mentions a 'wish-yielding' tree. The pure gold obtained from it is referred to as '*vogāntālakeśvara'* (98). *Haritālaka*, *haritāla* or *tālaka* is orpiment. Curiously enough the discussion then turns to the geo-nymic of '*tālaka*' - which is generally the term which referred to orpiment. Most probably this part has a '*Siddha tantra*' connection. '*Tālakeśvara*' is defined as a medicinal unguent in the Bhāva Prakāśa of Bhāva Miśra – a medieval lexicon. (99) But *tālaka* has also been used in the sense of orpiment in the Bhāva Prakāśa. (100).

The Suvraṇatantra manuscript under study mentions in this particular section five different types (names) of '*Dhatuvedhī*'. One is said to be known as *karṇâṭavgari*'. This is a clear reference to an alloy - the type which originated in the contemporary *Karṇâṭa* region. Medieval Karnataka and Tamil Nadu incidentally witnessed extensive innovations in metallurgy related to the alloying of beta bronzes for acoustic instruments, 'Damascus' Steel etc. The section goes on to describe that in the north it is known as "*siddhasvarṇa*", which might imply the substance, which gives success in transmuting gold. In the east this is (the *dhâtu* which in this composition is identified as some kind of dhātuvedhī or transmuting agent for metals) known as '*tâlaka*' – that is a clear reference to orpiment. In the west, it is said, the substance is known as '*dhâtuvedhī*'. (101) The reading of the entire description leads one to assume that the '*dravya*' whose nomenclature is being discussed here was a specific item known in different names in connection with every regional context. The term '*Dhātuvedhī*' would qualify for a substance that can, figuratively speaking, pierce a piece of metal' – literally perhaps meaning that it reacts with metals. Whether or not this is a direct reference to some kind of mineral solvent used by the contemporary metallurgists in mints or elsewhere is not certain. However, the reference to '*dhâtuvedhī*' and the regional names would imply some general practices, information of which was collected possibly by one (the composer of this text?) who was not himself properly conversant with either the substance or the techniques where the substance was applied. The nomenclature is also confusing. *Karnâṭa Vañgari or vôgari* would clearly refer to yellow orpiment from the region of Karanataka (south); *tâlaka* also to orpiment in general named in the east; *tâlakeśvara,* to some kind of medicinal unguent; *Siddhasvarṇòa* (name in the north) might mean a substance which transforms gold successfully; *dhâtuvedhî* (name in the west) is a clear reference to mineral solvent; "*kalyarakṣa*" (name in heaven) once more is probably a mythical term of reference. For other possibilities, see end note.(101a) Does this refer to a protective substance?(101 a) These were said to be the five names by which this particular substance was famously known all around. So for we could trace a logic in this description. But the next lines are confusing with multiple identifications, real and mythical, which are disconnected from the initial topic. "*Svarṇavimalâ*" - the sixth name was also known as "*tarurīti*". While "*svarṇavimalâ*" either refers to pure gold or to a substance that purifies gold, which is regarded as *Svarṇa vimalâ*, or, more probably - silver pyrite or pyrite of 3 kinds as identified in both P.C. Ray's work and the discussions in Mira Roy and B.V. Subbarayappa's work. *rīti* is of course brass and "*taru rīti*" (correct spelling: *krîti*') is told us as the term by which the substance was referred - *abhidhiyate*". (102).

Next follows some description of this (fictitous ?) '*taru*' and here the text turns truly esoteric in its meaning. Possibly some kind of magical and ritualistic significance is attempted here in order to keep to the growing esoteric tradition of siddhayoga. The plant, which is described here is said to have roots like the *śarkarākanda*– sugarcane (?) and leaves like the cotton tree – '*kārpāsa'*. Flowers and fruits are mentioned as '*lavālamāna*" – which are said to be considered as supernatural in nature – *"ca alaukikam matam"*. *Lavalî* is a fruit tree – Averrhoa Acida Viddh. (103) There is a significant reference to the fruit of the "*Lavalî* tree in Kalidasa's Vikramôrvaśîya– "*lavalīphala pāṇḍura*" - as pale as the fruit of the *Lavalî* tree".

The passages in this section prescribe that the branches of the above tree can be broken off and, re-planted – or grafted - leading to the growth of a new plant. It is most probably a reference to a 'bulbous' tree, which may be replanted from a leaf, bulb or stem. The juice of this plant is said to have significant reactions when mixed with any metal. The juice from its flowers is said to refine mercury- (*māraṇa* or killing of mercury) and not only that, *haritāla* and other such minerals (sulphide ores) are said to be killed in the same way.

Next follows a detailed instruction for the disciple/practitioner of alchemy: The Juice from the fruit of this plant is to be taken out with great care. Mercury should be rubbed with this juice for *triyâma* or nine hours. Then the mercury is to be put in a crucible and on roaring fire - *haṭâgni*. This refined mercury (*sûta*) helps attain "*kâmarûpa*" and is then prescribed as an elixir for youth and beauty – "*kâmarûpî bhabet sûta*" and also results in the individuals' transformation into black - haired charm - *kṛṣṇakeśî*.

The manuscript turns once more to metals and alchemy from the next passage. Mercury is said to help in attaining a hundred thousand times the qualities of any metal if rubbed with the juice of the leaf of this plant in a mortar for 24 hours.

Next section gives a very interesting observation on '*tâlaka*' or orpiment or more probably- the extract from orpiment – arsenic. The '*tâla*' is to be put carefully in a '*śaraba*' a container and killed. Then the orpiment is to be carefully put in an oven/ earthen - ware pot/temporary heating appliance - termed '*gajā*' (104) and heated.

The intake of this refined orpiment is said to be a certain cure for what is termed as '*rūddhā*' – '*tasya prabhakṣaṇāt putra rūddhā eva nāśayaḥ*'. The term '*rūddhā*' generally means obstruction. There is a reference to the particular ailment of urinary obstruction in the Suśruta as '*rūddhā mūtrā*' (105). However, we cannot be certain about the exact application here. This ingredient – mixed with any metal is said to enhance its qualities. First it is said to transform copper into gold - the colour of *Jâmbunada*. Orpiment in any case mixed with copper would result in an arsenic – bronze alloy. Next it is described that the juice mixed with *nāga* or lead (106) and *vaṅga* or tin would yield '*tāra*' or silver (tin and arsenic = pewter? or a tin-lead alloy?) – with the colour of '*kunda*' – silvery yellow. And all metals irrespective of their nature would be transmuted (dissolved?). Gold will attain the characteristic of gold. Silver will turn into silvery characteristics and the mercury will attain the characteristic of a hundred - fold of its transmuting power – or dissolving power.

Thus ended the "Siddha Vaṅgari Kalpa" or '*Siddha Vogari Kalpa*'

(Here the ms is so hazy that it is difficult to make out the letters) in fact the name or subject on which this section deals – is not clear. But probably there is a reference to a particular type of tree, the branches of which are to be used as fuel to burn a fire for killing mercury and orpiment (arsenic) – for refining these minerals. The mixture of arsenic – mercury then is to be thrown on any metal for transmutation. Copper is said to turn into gold, silver will remain silver, gold as gold. The first is without doubt a reference to bronze/ brass (if the given extract is included in the composer's general idea about '*pārada*' and '*tālaka*').

10. Dagdharuha Kalpam

The last section is on what is termed as "*dagdharûha*" – a burnt tree or, rather 'dagdhārohā', which has been identified by Mira Roy and B.V. Subbarayappa as Clerodendrum Phlomoides Linn (105a). This might also be an allegorical reference to the concept of how charcoal is formed. This might be clarified from further descriptions in this section. First the *śoka* advises that the wood of this tree is to be burnt into an ember (*aṅgâra*) and then this ember is to be planted – '*vâpayet*' =- which rather means that the ember is to buried under ground. The allegory here is that the buried ember will rise in a shooting plant. Five of the embers from this allegorical tree or rather five pieces of charcoal is to be mixed with mercury and orpiment. This mixture then is to be put into twentyone separate dishes (*puṭam*). Then all these (dishes with ingredient presumably are to be put on fire.) would be killed – "*mṛtyurbhaviṣyati*". It has not been clarified whether these dishes are put on an oven fire etc. However, the process referred to as "*mṛtyu*" in relation to metals denotes the "killing" or what is generally termed in the Rasaśâstra texts as "*mâraṇa*". Other terms often used for the same meaning are "*sūdana*" and "*hanana*" according to Mira Roy and B.V. Subbarayappa (107). "*Mâraṇa*" however, generally refers to the metallurgical process of purification of an ore. Here in this particular kalpa the reference is to what we presume to be the smelting process because of the description that follows. The next line describes that "*ta dvaya*" those two – (mercury and orpiment after being 'killed' in this fashion) – if thrown on any metal would immediately process the concerned metals into what is termed here as "*dhamayati*" - *dhamayat* meaning blown or melted (108) or because of the indirect allusion to charcoal – smelted. That ember wood is charcoal is also clear from the reference to buried burnt wood. Since the connection to the plant clerodendrum is implicit in the term 'dagdhārôgā,' it may not be for wrong to assume that the general belief was that the concerned burnt wood, ember or charcoal may have been originally the stalks of this species of plant. The text claims that the transformed/resultant metals are then turned into such excellence that they are known as "*sûrapûjite*" worshipped/ preferred even by gods. The next lines are more illustrative. It is mentioned that if copper is put in a crucible along with this ember, and here it is clearly mentioned that the crucible then is put on fire, the copper would definitely turn into gold. Next, it is proclaimed that this ember if powdered is enabled to transmute a hundredfold. Hot ember thrown on any metal would give the same result. Silver would attain the characteristics of silver - "*roupyatvamâyāti*"; gold would similarly attain "*svarṇatvamâyāyuḥ*" and in the last case it is mentioned that pure mercury is to be thrown into the crucible. The last line possibly refers to the process of amalgamation whereby mercury amalgamates with impure gold and pure gold is obtained. However, the manuscript is incomplete and stops at this line, leaving us to ponder upon what the complete text might have revealed to us – possibly the process of mercury – gold amalgamation and the extraction of gold.

The physical and/or chemical characteristics that make amalgamation work are not clearly understood to this day. However, it is known that if clean mercury is brought into contact with clean gold, the gold is wetted and "drawn into" the mercury. This results in a solution of gold in mercury or an alloy of gold and mercury called amalgam. After the mercury has gathered in the gold it can be removed by dissolving it in nitric acid or by driving it off as a vapor by heat. The gold will remain behind. The process involves: (1) liberation of the gold particles from the gangue; (2) removal of any coating which may be covering the gold; (3) keeping the mercury clean and bright; and (4) bringing the gold and mercury into intimate contact. Then the amalgam must be allowed to coalesce. Then the process requires one to separate it from the pulp and extract the gold. (109)

The Suvarnatantra, AS, MS. no. IM 5384, is thus an apparently difficult text to understand or rationalize. But it unfolds a world of knowledge and information, when read carefully and correlated with other sources of information on the traditions of Indian Āyūrveda and early medieval – medieval practices of metallurgy and chemistry. Alchemy, in terms of gold and immortality, the dream of the Rasāyana expert, was not attainable; but, in the process a lot of knowledge about metallurgical procedures, new alloys, new uses of minerals and plant extracts for both medicinal and metallurgical purposes were collected, probably observed and internalized – albeit often in a rather confusing manner. The Suvarṇatantra manuscript under study portrays the metallurgical aspect of alchemy much more than the rasāyana goal of attaining the elixir of life. The text is also quite shorn of pure metaphysical tone and makes only brief references to the God 'Śiva' as the Ultimate source of knowledge. The personality of Śiva could easily be transformed into that of a preceptor initiating a new trainee into the practice of alchemy. The language is simple and direct and there are little esoteric references except for the part where the working of pyrotechnology is indicated. This is rather revealing. The half – tone of knowledge regarding what is happening inside the closed oven during the process of curing mercury actually illuminates upon the composer's status as an outsider to the actual process of operation. The other sections where such mythical or estoteric references are alluded are the ones in Siddhasvarṇakalpa and to some extent the last kalpa. Here the allusions appear to enhance the magicality of the information being handed out, and may have been intended just so. On the other hand, the text does contain much information, in a garbled manner, of actual processes in brief outlines – as if these information have been passed on to the composer by an actual practitioner of the operations in bare outlines. The quality of language and condition of spellings in many cases would also indicate the low literary status of the composer. Reading between the lines the personality of the composer – the initiated in alchemy - unfolds as one from a common background of low means and high aspirations striving to get into the difficult business of chemical works related to what was understood as the magical discipline of alchemy in the medieval world, but what was actually grounded on a combination of the chemical applications in the twin domains of Āyūrveda pharmacology and metallurgy. In the process, this sixteenth century or there abouts text reveals unknown practices followed by the metallurgists, pharmacists and burgeoning chemists, not only in South Asia but in the medieval world of alchemy, encompassing China in the east and Arabic region in the West. The knowledge got transmitted among the worksmen and percolated, often in a confusing way, to the less specialized workrooms of the initiates in alchemy. It then found its way in an even more garbled form in the treatises composed by an aspirant to alchemy.

References

1. *Rasarnavakalpa*, edited and translated by Mira Roy and B.V. Subbarayappa, INSA, New Delhi, 1993 reprint.
2. Sir Monier Williams, *A Sanskrit-English Dictionary*, first published by Oxford University Press, 1899, 2002 edition, New Delhi Motilal Banarsiddass, Corrected, ed, - 2002 after Delhi report. **(after this referred as MW)**, Abbreviations, xxxv; 400.
3. For a discussion of the dates of the more well known lexicons vide Arthur A. Macdonell, *A History of Sanskrit Literature*, first ed, London, 1900, reprint consulted, Delhi, 1997, 368 – 369.
4. P.C. Ray, *A History of Hindu Chemistry, Combined edition of vol – I & vol – II,* Centenary edition, with a word by Syamal Chakrabarti, Kolkata, 2002, vol. II, 28 – 29.
5. The term refers to medicinal tablets.
6. This might be a reference to different sources of *haritāla* or arsenic, or, alternatively a reference to a myriad of ways in which *haritāla* was being used at the time.
7. MW describes '*kañjanī*' as Celastus Paniculatus, MW, 243.

7 (a) Tailakanda is identified as 'name of a bulb' in Monier williams Dictionary, 465

8. MW, 943.
9. Ibid.

10. Notes on the identification of this plant and possibilities of the accuracy of the information in the text: considering the repetitions on the poisonous nature of the *tailakanda*, any common variety of water lily – of nelumba or nymphaea would not fit the bill, for the bulbs of these lilies were actually edible and were eaten by the people in early India. An attempt to locate a water lily variety, which is described as poisonous landed up with the result that there is a species, the Nymphaea odorata Ait. Ssp. Tuberosa Paine) Wiersma and Hellquist variety, which is known as poisonous. When the seeds of this plant crowd together in the water body, they stimulate the production of ethylene gas. This species generally grows in acidic to alkaline waters. However, the species is native to North America and Mexico. It is not known whether the alkaline water with ethylene looks like a spread of oil in the surrounding water. Ethylene is a chemical compound with a formula C2H4. It is the simplest alkene. It reacts with water to produce ethanol - ethyl alchohol. The species Hydrocharis morsus – ranae, Ranaculus Scelera tus, and Regnellidium diphyllum, are also known to be stimulated by ethylene. There is really no proven clue to the actual species described here, or we cannot ascertain whether the description matches reality. The only information that is not riddled with confusing data is that this plant contained, or probably absorbed - an alkali or acid – like – halide nitrate or hydrochloride acids, which helped in the extraction of mercury. However, it is known that mercury (Hg) gets dissolved in water in gaseous form. A recent study carried out by a group of environmental scientists has proved that it is the mercurial emission that is embedded in the sediment, which is emitted in a diurnal cycle. Sediment incubation experiments carried out by this group suggest that the Hg^0 emitted from emergent macrophytes such as *Typha* and *Cladium* originates in the sediment. HgII in the rhizosphere is reduced to Hg^0 in these sediments by various processes, and is then transported by the plants to the atmosphere by two separate processes during the day and night. (Steve E. Lindberg, Weijin Dong, Jeff Chanton, Robert G. Qualls and Tilden Meyers, "A mechanism for bimodal emission of gaseous mercury from aquatic macrophytes", **Atmospheric Environment** , Volume 39, Issue 7, March 2005, Pages 1289-1301.) The fact remains that the aquatic plant roots and stems absorb and retain gaseous mercury throughout the day in some quantity. However, these facts may in no way be connected to the Tailakanda description.

11. The *Ain – i - Akbari* by Abul Fazl ' Allami, Complete English Translation, by H. Blochmann, Calcutta Madrasah, vol. I, Asiatic Society, Calcutta, 1873, Ain, 6.

12. Note on extraction of mercury: Mercury is a rare metal. Its ore is cinnabar, HgS, a red mineral occurring in fine granular massive form, often mixed with other materials. It was used as a cosmetic from the earliest times, and good crystals have been faceted as gems. Its crystals are rhombohedral, transparent to translucent, but very rare. It has a scarlet streak and perfect prismatic cleavage. The hardness of pure cinnabar is 2.5, and its specific gravity is 8.10. In spite of its heaviness, cinnabar in its usual form cannot be purified by panning, but responds to flotation. However, it is most economical to roast the unenriched raw ore with lime – calcium oxide, or iron or air, which oxidizes the sulphur to SO2 or FeS, and volatilizes the mercury, which is then condensed and collected. This reaction begins at about 250°C and is complete by 800°C. Mercury has a very simple metallurgy, and can be purified by distillation, unlike most other metals. Mercury can be obtained from cinnabar by heating the cinnabar ore in a current of air and condensing the mercury vapour formed. Due to its relatively low boiling point mercury can be easily purified by vacuum distillation.

Mercury is rarely found by itself in nature. Most mercury is chemically bound to other materials in the form of ores. The most common ore is red mercury sulfide, also known as cinnabar. Other mercury ores include corderoite, livingstonite, montroydite, and calomel. There are several others. Mercury ores are formed underground when warm mineral solutions rise towards the earth's surface under the influence of volcanic action. They are usually found in faulted and fractured rocks at relatively shallow depths of 3-3000 ft 1-1000 m). The process for extracting mercury from its ores has not changed much since Aristotle first described it over 2,300 years ago. Cinnabar ore is crushed and heated to release the mercury as a vapor. The mercury vapor is then cooled, condensed, and collected. Almost 95% of the mercury content of cinnabar ore can be recovered using this process. Because cinnabar ore is relatively concentrated, it can be processed directly without any intermediate steps to remove waste material.

The ore is first crushed and broken into smaller pieces. The crushed ore is then ground even smaller.The finely powdered ore is fed into a furnace or kiln to be heated. Some operations use a multiple-hearth furnace, in which the ore is mechanically moved down a vertical shaft from one ledge, or hearth, to the next by slowly rotating rakes. Heat is provided by fuel in the lower portion of the furnace or kiln. The heated cinnabar reacts with the oxygen in the air to produce sulfur dioxide - allowing the mercury to rise as a vapor.

This process is called roasting. The mercury vapor rises up and out of the furnace or kiln along with the sulfur dioxide, water vapor, and other products of combustion. A considerable amount of fine dust from the powdered ore is also carried along and must be separated and captured. As the oven cools, the mercury, which has a boiling point of 675° F 357° C), is the first to condense into a liquid, leaving the other gases and vapors to be vented. The liquid mercury is collected. Because mercury has a very high specific gravity, any impurities tend to rise to the surface and form a dark film or scum. These impurities are removed by filtration, leaving liquid mercury that is about 99.9% pure. The impurities are treated with lime to separate and capture any mercury, which may have formed compounds. In brief : In order to extract mercury from its ores, cinnabar ore is crushed and heated to release the mercury as a vapor. The mercury vapor is then cooled, condensed, and collected. References compiled from William Growland, The Metallurgy of the non-ferrous metals, London, 1914, 349; Carl Schuabel and Henry Louis, Handbook of Metallurgy, Translated by Henry Louis, London, 1907, 339; Izaak Maurits Kolthoff, Philip Juliber Elving, Treatise on Analytical Chemistry, New York, Part 2, Vol. I, 417.

The Rasarnava provides a clear information on the practice of mercury extraction current around the 11th – 12th centuries. The juice extracts from the plants - *Kākamaci, Jayā, Brāḥmi, Marjjari, Raktacitraka, Manduka, Mungaparni, Srngavera, Sasankaram, Devaḍāli, Sankhapuṣpi, Kākajanghā, Satāvari, Kumāri, Bhṛngarāja, Nirgunḍi, Gṛṣmasundaraḥ, Sulini, Suryaparni, Gojiḥvā, Kṣīrakañcuka* – are to be put in with cinnabar and ground in a mortar by which process the ore is freed of tin and lead – *vaṅganagou parityajya suddha bhabati sūtakaḥ* and becomes pure. (Rasarnava, edited by P.C. Ray and Haris Candra Kaviratna, Asiatic Society, Calcutta, 1910/1985 reprint, 154-155, 10th Patala, 55 – 56.) However, there is no mention of heating in a closed oven. This process is probably first mentioned in the Suvarnatantra ms under study here. The first Kalpa evidently takes great care to present the process of heating rasa in a closed oven with specific fuel. However, some mysticism has been added to the description which might have been due to either relatively poor understanding of the actual process of mercury extraction or deliberate aim to cloak the message in a shroud of esoterism.

13. This is a near probability. Orpiment cured in oil and mixed with copper ore would yield bronze of good lustre with a golden brown hue.

14. The tin and bell metal, with excess of orpiment /arsenic - would be rendered whiter.

15. "*Kharpara*' is identified as '*rasaka*' or calamine by Mira Roy and B.V. Subbarayappa, op. cit, New Delhi,1993, 135, 153. It is indicated that mercury, calamine with copper, zinc and arsenic orpiment, and the alkali of the plant root would turn into brass when heated. Silver turning into a golden metal with addition of only orpiment is unlikely. It is possible that copper and tin as well as silver and orpiment were put together - so that it would be a golden - white metal. Silver alloy forms available at present are Sterling Silver – an alloy of silver and copper, Brittannia silver with copper and Goloid with Silver, copper and gold.

16. '*udara*' - in Suśruta the term is used to mean the thick part of anything – MW, 184.

17. There is an allusion to '*ghorāghusyā*' under the term '*ghorā*' in the dictionary of Monier Williams and it applies to brass or bell metal or 'sounding dreadful', possibly referring to the sound emitted from brass and bell metal acoustics or objects, MW, 379.

18. "*cullikā*" - a term not commonly used in Sanskrit high language till the medieval period. The term '*cullī*' has been defined as a fire – place, MW, 400. It is interesting to note that the 11th century A.D. treatise on architecture: "Mayamata" contains a description of manufacturing a palanquin – the top portion of which is termed as "*culikā*". Incidentally, Bruno Dagens, who has translated the text, remarks that the identification of this term with the topmost part of a palanquin is not quite certain. Bruno Dagens, *Mayamatam*, vol. II, Indira Gandhi National Centre for the Arts, New Delhi, 1994/ 2000 reprint, Kalamulasastra Series, 15, f.n. on 724. Presumably the term '*culikā*' or '*cullikā*' denoted a shape of construction – possibly a pyramidical apparatus with a rounded top.

19. MW, 1287.

20. The firing ingredients mentioned here were not very common to the domestic purposes of the times when the text was being composed in approximately 16th – 17th Centuries.

21. MW, 912.

22. Mira Roy and B.V. Subbarayappa, *Rasarnavakalpa*, op. cit., INSA, New Delhi, 1993 reprint, appendix, 124.

23. P.K. Gode, *Studies in Indian Cultural History*, vol. I, Anangaranga folio 12b1-14 and Pancasayaka vol. 7b, 1-10.

24. MW, 244.

25. Note on extraction of silver: History

Silver was discovered after gold and copper about 4000 BC, when it was used in jewelry and as a medium of exchange. The earliest known workings of significant size were those of the pre-Hittites of Cappadocia in eastern Anatolia. Silver is generally found in the combined state in nature, usually in copper or lead mineralization, and by 2000 BC mining and smelting of silver-bearing lead ores was under way. Lead ores were smelted to obtain an impure lead-silver alloy, which was then fire refined by cupellation. (Compiled from material downloaded from http://dic.academic.ru/dic.nsf/enwiki/782138, on 13.3.2008; Medieval Method in Europe described in John Blair, Nigel Ramsay, English Medieval Industries, Craftsmen, Techniques, Products, London/Rio Grande, 1991, 110; also refer R.J. Forbes, Studies in Ancient Technology, Vol. VIII, Leiden, 2nd revised edition, (1964-72 for 9 volumes), 234-246 for ancient method).

Cupellation is a particular process of separating gold or silver from impurities by melting the impure metal in a cupel a flat, porous dish made of a refractory, or high-temperature-resistant, material and then directing a blast of hot air on it in a special furnace. The impurities, including lead, copper, tin, and other unwanted metals, are oxidized and partly vaporized and partly absorbed into the pores of the cupel. This process incidentally was known to the metallurgists since the Pre Harapan times and was most probably practiced in the Nal culture context in Baluchistan in the fourth millennium B.C. The production of heat resistant ceramics is also attested in the context of the Pre Harappan and Mature Harappan cultures. Vide J.H. Marshall, ed., Mohenjo – Daro and the Indus Civilization, Asian Educational Service reprint, New Delhi, 1996, 523-524; – Nupur Dasgupta, The Dawn of Technology on Indian Protohistory, Calcutta, 1997, 403, 411, 412, 419; Bridget Allchin, F.R. Allchin, Rise of Civilization on India and Pakistan, New Delhi, South Asian edition, 2003, 195; Jane Mcintosh, The Ancient Indus Valley, ABC CLI0, 189-190. Also for possibility of silver extraction vide U. Franke – Vogt, Excavation at Sohr Domb/Nal in 2002", in Franke – Vogt and J. Weisshaar, eds, South Asian Archaeology, 2003, 59, 72. However, it is imperative that some quality heat resistant ceramic containers were generally being used by the medieval metallurgists too. There is no particular reference to the use of any organic acid or alkali in the process. However, the description of '*kaṭu*' – refers generally to alkali in Āyurvedic tradition.

26. The nearest tin alloy that might be considered is the present - day Britannia metal, which is a pewter-type alloy with a silvery appearance and smooth surface, composition being 93% tin and 5% antimony, 2% copper. However, in general one may refer to the compositions of white metals. White metals may be both lead-based and tin-based alloys. Modern day white metal contains various permutations and combinations of antimony, tin, lead, cadmium, bismuth and Zinc. A number of metal items of medieval India (in museums) might be analyzed and found to have a high tin or lead content.

27. Henry Steel Olcott, "The Master of Djinns", *Old Diary Leaves,* Second Series 1878-83, Chapter XIX, 280 – 283, Theosophical Society in the Philippines, http://www.theosophy.ph/onlinebooks/odl/odl2toc.html. Downloaded on 13.3.2008.

28. Reference from Robert J. Silva, *Chemistry: Foundations and Applications*, 2004 "Translation", Findarticles.com, 26.12.2008.

29. Ladislao Reti, "Parting of Gold and Silver with Nitric Acid in a Page of the Codex Atlanticus of Leonardo da Vinci", *Isis*, Vol. 56, No. 3. (Autumn, 1965), pp. 307-319.

30. MW, 412.

31. Note: here the reference to *saptadhātu* and silver as a conglomerate clearly indicates that the idea of *astadhātu* prevailed behind these discussions. '*Pañcadhātu*' or '*Pañcalohā*' was commonly known to the early medieval and medieval metallurgists, especially in the Southern Indian context. It is an alloy of five metals. Pañchadhātu has been most widely used for making icons and idols. This five-metal combination of copper, gold, silver, lead and zinc, was considered to be a highly auspicious composition and is still used for icons cast for worship. In many cases it was referred to as '*aṣtadhātu*' - for example in early medieval and medieval Bengal, which in addition to pañcadhātu was said to include iron, tin and mercury. Practical compositions are combinations of either copper, gold, silver, lead and zinc; or copper, silver, lead, iron and tin; and also tin, copper, iron, lead and brass. The colour of the alloy is generally golden brown.

32. MW 862; There is a wild variety of pomegranate, Punica granatum L. Daroo, Daran, Darmu, used in traditional medicinal practices. Family: Punicaceae. GRIN Taxonomy, Also refer J. Morton, "Pomegranate", p. 352–355, in Julia F. Morton, ed, *Fruits of warm Climates*, Miami, FL. 1987.

33. One of the meanings of the descriptive term '*Gāńgeya*' is given as gold in the MW, 353. While gold was what was thought and desired to be the result of carrying out such a process, it was actually brass – the golden and shining alloy of copper, that might actually have been noted to have been produced by such a process. The addition of a plant alkaloid or acid could have been incidental.

34 Clearly neither mercury nor orpiment, but rather the extract of zinc or calamine is indicated here, which is often termed as '*rasaka*', vide P.C. Roy, op. cit, Calcutta, 2002, vol. I, 157; Mira Roy and BV. Subbarayappa, *Rasamavakalpa*, INSA, New Delhi, 1993 reprint, glossary 153. We have already referred to the methods of distillation of the calamine ore to obtain zinc as described in the Rasaratnasamuccaya of the 14th century as well as the physical evidence of zinc mining at the Zawar mines in Rajasthan in the

introductory chapter. It should also be mentioned here that many of the copper lead tracts in the mines of Chotonagpur Plateau also contain traces of zinc. Most mines that have veins of lead would also contain some amount of zinc. Copper, lead and zinc occurs together in Bhagalpur, Hazaribag, Munger, Palamau and Santal Parganas. D.K. Chakrabarti and N. Lahiri, *Copper and its Alloys in Ancient India*, New Delhi, 1996, 25.

35. MW, p. 860.

36. MW, p.1018.

37. B. V. Subbarayappa, "Transmutation: Ancient Indian Concepts and Practices", in *Prakriti*, General editor, Kapila Vatsyayana, vol. IV, J. Narlikar ed., Nature of Matter, Indira Gandhi National Centre of Arts, New Delhi, 1995; Mira Roy and BV. Subbarayappa, Rasarnavakalpa, INSA, New Delhi, 1993 reprint, glossary, 157.

38. P.C. Ray, op. cit., Kolkata, 2002, vol. I, 186 – 187.

39. Ibid, vol. II, 29.

40. Ahmad Y al - Hassan, "Transfer Of Islamic Technology To the West, Part III: Technology Transfer in the Chemical Industries", in A.Y. Al Hassan, A. Z. Iskandar and Maqbul Ahmed eds, *History of Science and Technology in Islam*, Part I, Ch. 1.5, in the multivolume series, *The Different Aspects of Islamic Culture*, UNESCO Project, 2002. Vol. IV.

41. *Masā'il / Risālat Mariyānus al-Rāhib al-hakīm lil-amīr Khālid ibn Yazīd* (MS A 70, item 19), Islamic Medical Manuscripts, National Library of Medicine, National Institute of Health, United States. This is the original MS on which Robert Chester composed his translation in 1144 A.D., with the title: "Liber de compositione alchimiae." However, the historical facts about this master personality in Arab alchemy tradition are quite confusing. Vide Raphael Patai, *The Jewish Alchemists: A History and Source Book*, Princeton University Press, 1994, 125 - 127. Therefore, it would be correct to assume that this knowledge had been attained in general among some of the experts among Arab alchemists in the seventh century A.D.

42. Kitab al-Khawass al-Kabir (the Great Book of Properties) of ibn Hayyan is one of his major works. It consists of 71 chapters on diverse subjects and 70 percent of these are chemical, industrial chemical or alchemical. Popular/accounts of Jabir's inventions refer to material originating mainly from this book. But no text from Kitab al-Khawass al-Kabir was ever edited or published. Only two manuscripts could be traced: British Library MS Or 4041 and Alexandria Municipality MS 5204. Jabir's Kitab al-Durra al-Maknuna which deals with coloured and lustre painted glass also deals in

chemical substances as understood at the time.

43. The above ms contains the . 1b-12a (item 1) *Kitāb al-Sirr al-sārr wa-sirr al-asrār* by Abu Bakr Muhammad Ibn Zakariyya al-Razi, (MS A 70, item 1, and the *Kitāb al-I hqāq min sab'īn* [extracts] by Jabir Ibn Hayyan, (MS A 70, item 4.)

44. The information in these manuscripts reveal that the knowledge of mineral based chemistry had advanced quite far among the Arab alchemists and probably among the Byzantine and Jewish alchemists of contemporary times too – as Raphael Patai points out, in Raphael Patai, *The Jewish Alchemists: A History and Source Book*, Princeton University Press, 1994, 125 - 127.

45. *Rasarnava*, ed P.C. Roy and Haris Candra Kaviratna, 1910/1985 reprint, Calcutta, IX, 2-3.

46. Vide, *Rasarnava*, op cit, VII, 12 – 13.

47. Mira Roy and B.V.Subbarayappa, *Rasarnavakalpa*, 7, main translated text, 68, Sanskrit verse, 105.

48. Index with Glossary, in *Rasarnava*, ed. P.C. Roy and Haris Candra Kaviratna, op. cit, 1985 reprint, 40.

49. Rasaratnasamuccaya, Book III, verses 127 – 129, edited original Sanskrit verses in P. C. Roy, op. cit., Kolkata, 2002, vol I. Sanskrit Texts, 36.

50. P.C. Roy, op. cit, 2002, vol. I, 96 – 7 cites **John Forbes Royle**, *An essay on the antiquity of Hindoo medicine : including an introductory lecture to the course of materia medica and therapeutics delivered at King's College*, London : W. H. Allen : J. Churchill, 1837, 40-41.

51. W. Clarke, *Natural History of Nitre*, London, 1670, 12 – 15, discusses that potassium nitrate was known as nitre since the days of Pliny the Elder.

52. James Riddick Partington with Contributor Bert S. Hall, *A History of Greek fire and Gun Powder*, John Hopkins University Press, 1998, 310 – 311.

53. Ibid, 204; Kitab Al-Furusiyya wa Al-Manasib Al-Harbiyya. (Book of Military Horsemanship and Ingenious War Devices) by Najm Al-Din Hassan Al-Rammah(1280), edited by Ahmad Yusuf Al-Hassan, University of Aleppo publications,1998.

54. Ahmad Y. Hassan, Potassium Nitrate in Arabic and Latin Sources, *History of Science and Technology in Islam*, UNESCO, 2002, Vol IV, part III; Ahmad Y Hassan, Gunpowder Composition for Rockets and Cannon in Arabic Military Treatises In Thirteenth and Fourteenth Centuries, ICON, vol. 9, 2004.

55. From the edited excerpt of the original Sanskrit verses of the "Suvarnatantra" mss in P.C. Ray, op. cit., Calcutta, 2002, vol. II, section on Sanskrit texts, 150 – 151.

56. *Ā'īn i Akabari A Gazetteer and Administrative Manual of Akbar's Empire and Part of History of India* by Abul Fazl Allami, Complete English translation, H. Blochmann, Asiatic Society, Calcutta, 1873, vol. I, Ā'īn 7, p. 25 of translation. Blochmann's footnote on this page mentions that the margins of the mss explain the word *ashkara* by the Hindi *sijji*, which was impure carbonate of soda.

57. *Refer P.C. Ray*, vol I: 174, Sukraniti, 201- 202; 176 – 177. The fourteenth century date for introduction of gun powder in ammunitions in India is clarified by Iqtidar Alam Khan, "Early Use of Cannon and Musket in India: A.D. 1442-1526", *Journal of the Economic and Social History of the Orient*, Vol. 24, No. 2. (May, 1981), pp. 146-164

58. P.C. Ray, op. cit., 2002, vol. I, 182 – 183.

59. Revere Academy of Jewelry Acts: The School of Jewelry Professionals. Internet Journal Ganoskin, Oct, 6, 2007, Bryn Morgen Press, Project. Prof. Dr. Erhard Brepohl. Also refer "Aqua Regia", Microf (R) Encarta (R) online Encyclopaedia 2008, 20th Dec.

60. Andrew Use and William Nicholson, *A Dictionary of Chemistry and Mineralogy: With their Applications*, Harvard University,1831.

61. British Pharmaceutical Codex, *An Imperial Dispensary for the use of Medical Practitioners and Pharmacists*,1911, digitalized version online, http://www.harvestfields.ca/British/index.htm.downloaded 26.4.2008.

62. Ibid.

63. *Salsola* Kali is a genus of herbs, subshrubs, shrubs and small trees in the family Amaranthaceae, native to Africa, Asia, and Europe; they typically grow on flat, often dry and/or somewhat saline soils, with some species in saltmarshes. The plant has great historical importance as a source of soda ash, which was extracted from the ashes of *Salsola soda* and other saltwort plants.Soda ash is one of the alkali substances that are crucial in glassmaking and soapmaking. Soda ash is now known to be predominantly sodium carbonate. In 1807, Sir Humphry Davy isolated a metallic element from caustic soda; he named the new element "sodium" to indicate its relationship to "soda.". This work is referred in his publication: *Elements of Agricultural Chemistry In A Course of Lectures*, London, Longman, 1813. The ashes obtained by the burning of *Salsola soda* can be

refined to make a product called soda ash, which is one of the alkali materials essential to making soda-lime glass, soap, and many other products. The principal active ingredient is sodium carbonate, with which the term "soda ash" is now nearly synonymous. The processed ashes of *Salsola soda* contain as much as 30% sodium carbonate.A high concentration of sodium carbonate in the ashes of *Salsola soda* occurs if the plant is grown in highly saline soils (i.e. in soils with a high concentration of sodium chloride), so that the plant's tissues contain a fairly high concentration of sodium ions. Cited in Archibald Clow and Nan. L Clow, (1952). *Chemical Revolution,* Ayer Co Pub, June 1952, pp. 65-90; Integrated Taxonomic Information Service (2007). "*Salsola soda L.*," report for taxonomic serial number 504989, retrieved May 19, 2007; T. Barker, R. Dickinson and D. W. F. Hardie 1956. "The Origins of the Synthetic Alkali Industry in Britain," *Economica, New Series*, Vol. 23, No. 90. (May, 1956), pp. 158-171.

64. Solanum surratense Burm. f. : Common Names: Yellow-berried nightshade, Kanthikari, Chitrankaayi, Kandankathiri. Medicinal Uses: Fruits eaten as an anthelmintic and for indigestion. Root is an expectorant, used in Āyurvedic medicine for cough, asthma, chest pain. Also used for flatulence, sore throat, and toothache. Has high concentration of solasodine, a starting material for the manufacture of cortisone and sex hormones. D.B. Deb, "Solanaceae in India", in J.G. Hawkes et. al., eds., The biology and taxonomy of the Salanaceae. (Bio Solan) 105; For Indian species information refer http://hpforest.nic.in/VanVihar.htm. Website of Himachal Pradesh Forest Department downloaded on 26.4.2008.

65. Inula racemosa (Hook.f) is a member of the Asteraceae family. It grows in the temperate and alpine western Himalayas, and it is common in Kashmir. The roots are widely used locally in indigenous medicine as an expectorant and in veterinary medicine as a tonic. This herb contains insulin (10%) and has an essential oil, containing alantolacetone, which is strongly anthelmintic. This herb helps pulmonary functions, the blood, and general health of individuals. Cited in http://www.scs.unr.edu/~pelges/rpindex.htm,downloaded on 26.4.2008 and Dr. G. Singh. and Prof. Dr. P. Kachroo, *Forest Flora of Srinagar.* Bishen Singh Mahendra Pal Singh, 1976.

66. *Ferula rubricaulis* is a south Persian plant, probably growing to some extent in northern Persia also. Range: W. Asia - Central Iran, Turkey and southern Russia. Its habitat is the herbaceous slopes in the steppes. Vide R.A. Donkin, *Manna: A Historical Geography*, Bio Geographia, vol. 17, Kluwer Academic Publishers, 1980, 26 – 39. The plant from which the gum-resin *Galbanum* is

obtained was not definitely known at the time. The *British Pharmacopoeia* (The British Pharmacopoeia, 1898 published under the Direction of the General Council of Medical Education and Registration of the United Kingdom [1898], London, 1898) mentions the above-named species and refers to the probability of other species of *Ferula* yielding it. That the *Ferula galbaniflua* is believed to yield it is due to the statement of F. A. Buhse, a German resident of Persia, who relates that in 1848 (Flückiger, 1891), he was informed that the product spontaneously exudes from the plant in question, and was told by the natives that it was the source of galbanum. Galbanum is imported from the Levant, and from India in cases and chests. It is generally met with in lumps, consisting of large, irregular masses of a brownish or dark-brownish color, and composed of agglutinated tears, some few of which, when broken, are somewhat translucent; they have a waxy density, but become soft and sticky at a temperature of 35° to 37.7° C. (95° to 100° F.), are not pulverizable unless in very cold weather, have a strong, unpleasant odor, and a hot, somewhat acrid, and amarous taste. Occasionally, galbanum is met with in the form of oval, globular, or irregular tears. On account of the impurities it contains, it should be melted and strained previous to employing it. When the color of galbanum is dark-brown or blackish, and when it contains an admixture of sand, straw, chips of wood, and other foreign matters, the article should be rejected as being inferior. The specific gravity of galbanum is 1.212. Galbanum is partially dissolved by water, vinegar, or wine, forming therewith an emulsion. Alcohol dissolves about three-fifths of it, the residue being gum and impurities. Diluted alcohol is its best solvent. Chemical Composition.—According to Pelletier, galbanum contains 6 per cent volatile oil, 67 per cent resin, 19 per cent gum, and 8 per cent foreign matter (H. and H). Pelletier's findings reported in E. Chambers, Chamber's Encyclopaedia: A Dictionary of Universal knowledge for the People, J.B. Lippincott Co., 1870, Vol. I, 470. The *volatile oil* consists mainly of a hydrocarbon of the terpene series, $C_{10}H16$. According to Mössmer its boiling point is between 160° and 165°C. (320° and 329° F). Mössmer findings reported in E. Gildemeister, F. Hoffmann, E. Kremers, The Volatile Oils, Pharmaceutical Review Pub. Co., 1900, 576. It is dextro-rotatory, colorless, has a specific gravity of 0.884, and forms crystals with gaseous hydrochloric acid. Probably other hydrocarbons are also present. The yellow-brown *resin* of galbanum may be obtained (Flückiger, *Pharmacognosie*, 1891, p. 65), by extracting galbanum with alcohol and distilling off the solvent. The residual resin is also soluble in carbon disulphide in commercial but not quite in absolute ether, and in caustic soda. Upon destructive distillation galbanum resin yields an aqueous fraction containing fatty acids, and a thick blue oil of the composition $C_{20}H_{30}O$, or more probably $C_{10}H_{16}O$, after removing therefrom a hydrocarbon C_{30}H48 (Kachler, 1871). J- Kachler. ... (Annalen der Chem. i<. Pharm. Sept. 1871, Bd. 159, S. 281 — 304). The blue oil boils at 289° C. (552.2° F.), and holds in solution or suspension a crystalline body which Sommer (1859) named *umbelliferon*. This substance is a common constituent of the products of the dry distillation of such gum-resins as asafoetida, sagapenum and opopanax, and those derived from *Imperatoria Ostruthium*, *Angelica Archangelica*, etc. The plant morphology, chemistry and medicinal uses had been first recorded in *King's American Dispensatory, 1898, written by Harvey Wickes Felter, M.D., and John Uri Lloyd, Phr. M., Ph. D.* King's American Dispensatory is a 2 volume work first published in 1854 that covers the uses of herbs used in American medical practice, especially by those involved in Eclectic medicine which was the botanical school of medicine in the 1800s-1900s. In 1880 John Uri Lloyd, without a doubt, the most famous and accomplished eclectic pharmacist of the late nineteenth and early twentieth centuries, promised his friend, Professor King, to revise the pharmaceutical and chemical sections of the American Dispensatory. Eighteen years later an entirely rewritten eighteenth edition (third revision) was published in 1898. It was co-authored by eclectic physician Harvey Wickes Felter, M.D. A 1922 reprint of the 1898 edition can be found on Henriette Kress' encyclopedic herbal website; Properties of Ferula also referred in Friedrich August Flückiger, *Pharmacognosie des Pflanzenreichs*, 3rd ed., Berlin, 1891, p. 65. Some details are also found in Robert Bentley, Henry Trimen, Medicinal Plants, Being Descriptions with Original Figs. of the Principal Plants Employed of Medicine an Account of the characters, Properties and uses of their Parts and Products of medicinal value, London, J. A Churchill, 1880/Asiatic Publishing House, 2002 reprint, Vol. I, 128. Also referred in Berthold Laufer, Sino-Iranica: Chinese Contributions to the History of Civilization in 1919, Field Museum of Natural History, Original from Harvard University. Digitized 20 Dec 2007, 379 – 384. In India an old report is found Mordecai Cubitt Cooke, Report by Dr. M.C. Cooke, on the Oil Seeds and Oil in the Indian Museum, Or Produced in India, Published by Indian Museum, 1876, Calcutta, 58, digitised. Cooke also refers to Buhse's encountering the Ferula gum. However, how for these plant sources were useful for extracting salts is not clear, apart from the early historical information in the Suśruta Samhita.

67. MW 244, Mira Roy and B.V. Subbarayappa, op. cit., 1993 reprint, 124.
68. the term '*pittala* was a later, probably medieval nomenclature.
69. A mythical river Jambunada is the river of fables flowing from the mount Meru, MW, 412. Vana upala literally means forest stones. This specification might actually refer to charcoal and the nomenclature indicates that the alchemists had noted the origin of charcoal from wood.

69a. The root 'dhma' or 'dham' - dhamati refers to kindling of fire by bellowing worthy in association with smelling or melting of metals, M.W. 509.

70. Discussed above.
71. MW, p. 355.
72. MW, p. 858.
73. MW 929.
74. Suśruta, Saṁhitā, Sūtrasthānam, Ch. XXXVIII, 35.
75. Incidentally, a term - 'tāmra vallī' has also been listed under the definition for the term 'Tālaka' in the Monier Williams Dictionary p. 445, which refers to a plant - Curculigo orchoides L. This species was long considered as an important herb source for Āyurvedic medicine. Curculigo orchoides (Taalmuli) is found in places that are up to 6000 feet above sea level and is commonly seen in south India. The rhizomes are used and are known vata and pitta suppressant and kapha aggravator. This herb is mostly indicated as an aphrodisiac and can increase sperm count and prevent impotence. It is a good preventative for skin ailments, digestive problems, and respiratory disorders. A good general health tonic. This plant has a long and continuing history of use as a medicinal ingredient. For example, the article "Direct *in vitro* regeneration of *Curculigo orchoides* Gaertn., an endangered anticarcinogenic herb", published in the section: Scientific Correspondence, CURRENT SCIENCE, VOL. 84, NO. 6, 25 MARCH 2003, (http: // www. iisc.ernet.in/currsci/mar252003/747.pdf. downloaded on 26.4.2008) refers to this species as an endangered anticarcinogenic plant. Incidentally this rhizomehad been used and referred as a medicinal plant in ancient China and India. Rhizoma Curculiginis (Xian Mao) had been registered in ancient Chinese classic texts like *Lei Gong Pao Zhi Lun* (Lei's techniques for Processing herbs), Su Gong's pharmacology, *Nan Hai Ben Cao* gangmu (Collection of Materia Medica) and Shi Zhi Ben Cao (A Food treatment Materia Medica) and other works of Jiang

Qing-yun, Tu-jin Bencao and Zhu Zhen-Heng Ben cao, etc. on medicine, herbs and pharmacy. The first text marks the earliest notice and this text noted that Rhizoma Curculiginis (Xian Mao) grow in the region of Xi Yu, in the state of Shu. The text of *Tu Jing Ben Cao* noted that Rhizoma Curculiginis (Xiam Mao) grows in the Xi Yu and Da Yu Mountains, and is cultivated at Shu Chuan, Jiang Hu, Zhe and other provinces. Leaf is described as blue as thatch grass and soft, wider in middle part, grows vertical surface texture is like the leaf of palm. The plant dries up in winter, grows in the next spring - blooming in March, as Gardenia yellow. It does not bear fruit. Rhizoma is single rooted and erect. The colour of the root appears yellow to white, outer skin of the root is brown. The root which is the main ingredient for medicinal use is generally dug out in the months of February or August and dried in the sun. It is a small perennial herb, *Habitat:* mountain grassland, taste bitter sour, contains hydroxy methyl, The chloroform extract indicated the presence of alkaloids. In Indian Āyūrveda tradition this species is known as Talmuli or commonly called Kali Musli at present.. The plant is rare and found in the region of Southern India and Chattisgarh. Indian evidence cited in S.P. Agharkar., (1991), *Medicinal plants of Bombay presidency*. Pbl. Scientific publishers, Jodhpur, 81-82; U Singh, A.M Wadhwani and B.M Johri, *Dictionary of economic plants of India*. Pbl. Indian Council of Agricultural Research, New Delhi, (1996), 62; P.S. Varier,. *Indian Medicinal Plants: A compendium of 500 species*, Orient Longman, Hyderabad, 1995, Vol - II: 245 - 248.

76. MW 1106.

77. This identification is provided in the Jayvir Anjaria, Minoo Parabia, Gauri Bhatt and Ripal Khamar, eds. 2002, *Nature Heals : A Glossary of selected Indigenous medicinal plants of India*, SRISTI, 16.

78. Mira Roy and BV Subbarayappa, op.cit., 1993 reprint, New Delhi, 159.

79. MW, 1106.

80. MW, 291.

81. *rasaka* mentioned in Mira Roy and Subbarayappa, op. cit., Glossary, 153.

82. MW, 869.

83. MW, 870.

84. MW, 1255.

85. MW, 272.

86. MW, 217.

87. MW, 218.

88. Ibid.

89. MW 364.

90. Brhat Samhitā, Ch 1xxvi, 10.

91. MW, 1106.

92. The roots of Kustha contain resinoids, essential oil, alkaloid, inulin, a fixed oil, some minor amount of tannins and sugar. www.himalayahealthcare.com/aboutĀyūrveda/cahs.htm. It is a commonly used medicinal herb in China and is considered to be one of their 50 fundamental herbs. It is also used in Āyurvedic medicine where it is valued mainly for its tonic, stimulant and antiseptic properties. It is said to be aphrodisiac and to be able to prevent the hair turning grey. J. A. Duke. and E. S. Ayensu, *Medicinal Plants of China,* Reference Publications, Inc., 1985; A. Chevallier, *The Encyclopedia of Medicinal Plants,* Dorling Kindersley. London, 1996. According to H. Panda, Kustha or Puskarmul contains two liquid resins, an alkaloid, a solid resin, salt of valeric acid, an astringent principle and its ash contains manganese. Its root extract contains terpee alcohol, alkaloid Saussurine, etc. H. Panda, 1999, *Herbs Cultivation and Medicinal Uses,* National Institute of Industrial Research, 540.

93. MW 1215.

93a. MW, 266.

93b. Ṣaṣthi Mukha may be read as ṣaḍmukha which is defined as Siva with six faces, M.W. 1109. Mercury and Śiva have been identified in Indian alchemy tradition. So far as the term 'siddheśvara' in connection with alchemy is concerned, there is one conjuncted word : "Siddhauṣadhika by which a collection of five drugs is referred : tailakanda, sudha-k, kroda-k, rudantika and sarpa netra. Please note the connections to tailakanda and sudha. MW, 1216.

94. MW, 696, verb root '*pras*' from *Dhatupath*, xix, 4, '*prasate*': to spread, extend, diffuse. Here it might refer to the process of dilution with a thousand parts of solution – '*prasya sahasram*'.

95. Time measurement - a period of 3 hours-MW – 850.

96. MW 443, Bhāva Prakāśa – IV, 6, 27.

97. MW, 444.

98. Corrected reading – *vangaritālakeśvara* – the term '*vangari*' denotes yellow orpiment, MW, 912, while '*tālakeśvara*' denotes a medicinal unguent. On the other hand '*tālaka*' again denotes orpiment. '*tālakeśvara*' might have been a preparation involving the use of orpiment.

99. M W, p. 445.

100. Bhāva Prakāśa v, 26, 48, 221. referred in MW, 445.

101. Joseph P.R. James, "Process of Producing Shell Powders", US Patent No. 801, 317, Patented Oct. 10, 1905, from htt;:// www.gogle.co.in/patents?hl = enlr = vid = USPAT801317 id = AQAAAAEBAJ oi.downloaded on 24.12.008. Mineral solvent or aqua fortis or a transmuting agent for metals. Monier Williams dictionary refers to "mixture of fluids" as one of the meanings of the term "*vedhī*" MW, in 1018.

101a. 'Kalya' - one of the definitions is put as 'health' and 'harītakī' Emblic Myrobalan, M.W., 263. A very interesting and probably relevant reading of the term 'Kalyarakṣa' would be to interpret it as an alternative term for 'Kaladhūta meaning silver in MW, 266; and 'Kaladhauta' meaning gold and silver, MW, 266. If 'kala' or 'kalya' would be taken as silver or gold, then kalýa rakṣa would be the 'protector' or 'purifier' of gold and silver.

102. In brief, the description might refer to a substance that purifies gold, or dissolves it. On the other hand, orpiment and brass are also indicated. Furthermore, 'Vimalā' has been defined as silver gilt in M./w, 979. P.C. Ray describes 'Vimalā' in connection with 'chemistry in Rasaratnasamuchchaya, where vimalā' has been identified as of 3 types according as it has the lustre of gold, silver and brass. The Rasaratnasamuccaya refers to the process of killing vimalā by roasting the mineral ten times with sulphur, bitumen and artocarpus lakoocha plant and the acids - by doing which there appears a gold-like essence — P.C. Ray, Op. Cit, Kolkata, 2002, Vol. I, 84-85; Mira Roy and B.V. Subbarayappa, Op. cit., New Delhi, 1993, Glossary, 156 describes 'Vimalā' as silver pyrites and also pyrites with golden hints which have been also mentioned in Ayūrveda prakāśa and Rasajalanidhi.

104. "A small hole in the ground for a fire (over which to prepare food or medicine)" – MW, 342.

105. MW, 884.

105a. Mira Roy and B.V. Subbarayappa, op.cit., New Delhi, 1993, Glossary, 141.

106. MW, 533.

107. Mira Roy and B.V. Subbarayappa op. cit., New Delhi, 2003, p. 150.

108. MW, 510.

109. Amalgamation is a concentrating process in which metallic gold or silver, or an alloy of the two, is mixed with mercury, either in a amalgamation drum, or on a amalgamation table, where the precious metal bonds with the mercury to form the metal laden

mercury AMALGAM and the waste (barren) ore pulp are caused to travel different paths to effect separation. The ore containing the precious metals should be ground fine enough to allow the maximum exposure of the gold or silver surface to the mercury (usually between 100 mesh and 325 mesh). Often, water is used as the ore is mixed with water to help disperse the ore and to promote a better precious metal to mercury interface.

Sulfide precious metal ores are difficult to amalgamate using mercury, due to the complex iron-sulfur-gold and other metals present, which do not allow the gold to come into contact with the mercury. It is not uncommon for only 20% to 30% recovery of gold and silver by mercury amalgamation. Precious metals are recovered from the mercury by retorting the mercury. Retorting consists in distilling off the mercury from the amalgam and is done in a cast iron retort or steel retort, a vessel having a cover which can be fastened on so tightly that no fumes of mercury escape, except by the condenser, which leads from the cover to a vessel containing water, where the fumes of mercury are condensed to a metallic state. The condenser has a water jacket surrounding it, through which a small quantity of cold water is continuously passed during the operation. The open end of the vapor pipe must be lower than where it emerges from the discharge of the retort, and its open end is submerged in water during the distilling operation. The retort should not be filled much over half full, of amalgam, as room is required for the vaporized mercury. It is good practice to make the amalgam into several small balls, thus allowing the mercury to vaporize more rapidly. The distillation is performed at a very low temperature and heat applied very gradually, until 1,500 deg F is reached. It usually takes 2 hours to retort the amalgam, once the 1500 deg F temperature is reached. Information is from Leonard J. Goldwater, *Mercury: A History of Quicksilver*, York Press, Baltimore, MD, 1972; *The Wordsworth Dictionary of Science and Technology*, 1995 edition, Wordsworth editions Ltd, Hertfordshire, 28.

In the 2nd century AD China, an alternative large scale manufacturing process for gold powder was proposed by Hu Gangzi. He invented a chemical method for making gold or silver powder, in addition to the comminution method mentioned above. He belonged to the later part of the second century A.D. in the Later Han period. This excellent chemical method was described in 'Chu Jin- Kuang Tu-Lu', a well known book. Reference in K. Zhao, '*Studies in the History of the Natural Sciences*' (in Chinese), 1984, 3 (3), 224, cited in *Zhao Huaizhi and Ning Yuantao,* "Techniques Used for the Preparation and Application of Gold Powder in Ancient China", ***Gold** Bulletin,* 2000, **33**(3), 104; Ho Peng Yoke, *Li Qi and Shu: An Introduction to Science and Civilization in China*, , 1985, University of Hong Kong, Courier Dover Publication, 2000, 176 – 177.

SELECT LIST OF PLANTS MENTIONED IN THE MANUSCRIPT AND CHAPTER V

- *kamala I Kañja* – Nelumbo nucifera Gaertn; Nymphaea Lotus L.
- *Vamśa* – Bambusa vulgaris
- *Khadira* – Acacia Catechu (WILLD)
- *Kaṭukuṣmāṇḍa – a variety of kusmanda*
- *Kuṣmāṇḍi/kuṣmāṇḍa* – Benincasa cerifera Savi / Benincasa hispida (Thunb.) Cogn.
- *Kaṭucaturjātaka:*
  (*a*) cardamoms – Eletteria cardamomum Maton / Amomum aromaticum ROXB. Bengal cardamom.
  (*b*) bark of Laurus cassia L. or Cinnamomum cassia (BLUME)
  (*c*) leaves of Laurus nobilis L.
  (*d*) black pepper – Piper nigrum L.
- *Pattraka* - Laurus Cassia L.
- *Raktabīja* – Punica granatum L.
- *'Kundapuṣpa'*
  (*a*) jasmine jasminum multiflorum or pubescens
  (*b*) fragrant oleander- white variety of Nerium oleander L. or Nerium indicum Mill.
  (*c*) or if only '*kunda*' is implied - the resin of the plant . Boswellia thurifera ROXB.
- *Mālati* Jasminum sambac or Nyctanthes sambac.
- *Mālati or śigru* - Moringa Oleifera Blanco or Lam. or Moringa pterygosperma Gaertn.
- *Eranḍa* - Ricinus communis Linn.
- *kadalī* - banana - Musa sapientum – Kuntze
- *Arka* - Calotropis Gigantea L. R. BR.
- *Suvarcala* – Ruta graveolens Linn.; Salsola kali Linn.; Cleome gynandra Linn.
- Paracoto - a species of *Cryptocarya* /Laurineae/ *Aniba coto*
  Kanṭakāri – Solanumin indicum L.
- *Puṣkarmūl* – Inula Racemosa (Hook.f) or *Puṣkarmūl*
- Ferula Galbaniflua Boiss.
- *Kaṭutumbī*" - Lagenaria vulgaris Seringe.
- *Śvetā*
  (*a*) A small white shell or cowry.

(*b*) Names of various plants, in different texts not recorded in published dictionaries.

(*c*) The birch tree.

(*d*) A white bignonia – Boerhavia Procumbens Roxb, or Boerhavia diffusa L. – *Punarnava.*

(*e*) Achyranthes Atropurpurea. Linn identification Achyranthes aspera. L.

- *Girikarṇī* - Alhagi Maurorum L.
- *'Vallī'* or *'vallī pañcamūla'*—

(*a*) *vidari* – Ipomoea digitata Linn.

(*b*) *sārivā* – Hemidesmus indicus R. BR.

(*c*) *rajani* – Curcuma longa Linn

(*d*) *Ajā Śṛngī* - Gymnemna sylvestre R.

- *Tāmra vallī* - Curculigo orchoides L.
- *Aparājitā* – Clitoria Ternatea Linn.
- *Gokṣura* - Tribulus terrestris L.
- *kustha* - Saussurea lappa C.B. Clarke
- *Śālmolī* - Bombax ceiba L./ Bombax malabaricum Candolle; Gossampinus malabarica (Candolle) Merrill; Salmalia malabarica (Candolle) Schott & Endlicher.
- Source of *karpura* - Cinnamomum camphora (L.) J. Presl
- *Kāka* and *kākari, Kākoli*

(*a*) *Raktika* - Ardisia humilis vahl.,

(*b*) Abrus Precatorius Taub.,

(*c*) Ficus oppositifolia L.,

(*d*) Solanum indicum L.

– are all listed under '*kāka*'.

- *Śarkarā* - sugarcane – Saccharum officinarum Linn, *kanda* – stalk or root of sugarcane.
- *Kārpāsa* – Gossypium indicum/ Gossypium herbaceum
- *Lavalī* - Averrhoa Acida L. or Viddh. - mentioned as Averrhoa acida Phyllanthi species in the Linnean Collection list pblshed online by the Linnean Society of London. The species is said to be annotated by Christen Früs Rottboell / Averrhoa carambola Linn. Could also be Phyllanthus acidus/distichus – in Sanskrit – Panduphala; also identified as Annona reticulata by some.
- *Dagdhārohā* – Clerodendrum multiflorum (Burm F.) O. Ktze./ Clerodendrum Phlomoides Linn. Alternative Sanskrit name Kṣudra Agnimantha.

6

TRANSLATION OF SUVARNATANTRA

Sutapa Saha

The entire edifice of ancient man and medicine is based on the concept of the fundamental identity between Man and Nature.[(1)] Man is considered as to be the microcosm of the macrocosm, both being constituted by the Pancabhutas- namely, prithvi (earth), ap (water), agni (fire), vāyu (air), ākaśa (space), each of which has been perceived by their distinctive quality.[(2)]

Āyūrveda or the science of longevity was a need-based, utilitarian science, in ancient India, famous for its healing effect on the body which obviously touched the soul, for Āyūrveda describes the well-being of a person both in physical and mental sense. Śuśruta Samhita, a text on medicine, defines a healthy person as—"Samodoṣaḥ samāgniścha samadhātumanāśrayaḥ / Prasannātmendriyamanaḥ swastha iti abhidhiyate" that is, one whose doṣas, agni, body elements and excretory functions are harmonious and whose self, mind and senses are cheerful is said to be healthy.

However, our main concern is not to do with these aspects of Āyūrveda. On the contrary, our interest rests on the substantial number of treatises which deals with Rasāyana, which contains discussions on different organic and inorganic substances, their medicinal values and compositions of concoctions for different purposes. This part also deals with the preservation of youthfulness and prolongation of life and also preservation of strength, memory power, brain power and the power of all sense organs.

Alchemy is said to have flourished in the medieval period and numerous alchemical (rasavidya) texts were written between the ninth and the fourteenth centuries A.D.... The texts on Indian alchemy reveal that a wide variety of organic and inorganic substances were used, plant as well as animal products, but more of the former. The important minerals are generally referred to as rasas, classified as mahā (superior) and upa (subsidiary) rasas. Mercury, though a metal, is extolled as the king of rasas, the mahārasa and has several names in the rasaśāstra texts: pārada, sita, rasendra, svarṇakāraka (maker of gold), sarvadhātupati and, more significantly, in a mythological setting, śivaja (born of Śiva) Śiva virya (semen of Śiva) and Haravīja (seed of Śiva). More than two hundred names of plants have been mentioned in the texts, but many of them have not been properly identified from the point of view of modern botanical nomenclature.(3)

The alchemical texts written in the medieval period primarily dealt with the gold-making and elixir-synthesis .Elixir or Rasāyana was a substance that could transform other base metals into gold and silver, as well confer longevity and immortality when taken internally. If an elixir proved successful in transmutation of metals it was supposed to be safe for internal administration as well.(4) Owing to its heavy weight, silvery white and shiny appearance, fluidity, and its property of readily combining with other substances, mercury was considered as the most potent of all substances and as possessing divine properties.

Of this property of Mercury, of having divine quality of transmuting metals into gold, we are not very sure in respect to modern science. It is known from modern chemistry that mercury is the liquid metal, very poisonous in nature, unstable in character, and when reacting with any other baser metal takes into the property of that metal into it , owing to its heavy weight . The alchemists of ancient India, were either aware of its destructive characteristic, so attributed mercury with divine qualities or perhaps mercury really had the quality to transmute baser metals into gold stills remains a question and needs testing. It is said that mercury has to undergo eighteen processes before it could be used for transforming either metals or human body.

However, Suvarṇatantra, the manuscript of our concern, is possibly an alchemical text which is estimated to belong to the sixteenth century A.D. The text does not clearly mention its date or its authorship. A certain name, Maheśwar, has been found but its credibility is not certain for the text starts in a dialogue form between Śiva and Paraśurāma. Śiva could be called as Maheśwara as well. One is not very sure about it but several references of the same name has been found in the text. The name of the scribe has been found to be Raghunath Sharma. But again one could not be certain about it.

The text, however mentions various chemical applications and its uses. The use of metals, their colour and various formations are ascribed in the manuscript, that is, lôhita, tāmra, kāñcana, pārada. The manuscript is also important for its vivid analysis of metals, processing and mixing, oxidation process. The merits of herbal tablets have been stated as well. The ms relates that over six hundred verses has been stated in various texts on the use of mercury. Regarding the mode of its use, the text vaguely mentions the proportions but it could not be utilized in the proper way.

The author of the text presents his discourse by paying homage to Lord Gaṇeśa in the beginning and then to Lord Śiva whose intellect was supreme. The MS starts with: "Śrī Paraśurāma uvāca / Devadeva Mahādeva ṛddhi buddhi phala prada / Purvam saṁsucita ṛddhi Rasāyana parā varā".

These lines means, Śrī Paraśurāma pays homage to the God of all Gods, Mahādeva, who is full of wisdom and knowledge and the mentioned wisdom is Rasāyana which is for all. Rasāyana or chemistry is mentioned as the first and foremost subject. Not only that, the text emphasizes that the practice of that subject makes a man free from kṣaya, that is perishing. Actually the knowledge of rasa, that is, liquid, bodily secretion, exudation, taste, flavour was very important for a man for day to day practice.

The text also informs us the various means of chemical elements used in our daily life in different processes and purposes. The author also presents the discourse and medicinal use of gold as a part of a whole series on the use of metals and ores in the traditional medicine.

The chemistry found in Suvarṇatantra deals with gold-making and elixir synthesis. The MS(manuscript) so states that Paraśurāma having given away his worldly possessions to Kāśyapa, is rendered destitute and thus has to invoke the aid of Lord Śiva for his very maintenance. This is found in the ślôka where mention of bhūmi-dāna and bhūmi-bhāga has been referred to as means of measurement.—"Bhūmidānam mayā dattaṁṛṣye kaśyapāya vai / kāśyapenāpyahạm prôktô bhūmibhāgam tyājo prabhô".

Hence to help Parasūrāma, Lord Śiva utters that he would relate a tantra which will speak about the mystery of mysteries named Svarṇatantra as found in the ślôka__"Śrṇu Rāma (Lord Śiva saying to Paraśurāma) pravakṣyāmi rahasyati rahasyakam / Svarṇatantrabhidham tantram kalpa rūpeṇa kathyate.

Hence starts the chapters (kalpas) of Svarṇatantra. The MS specifies several chapters on the transmutation process and methods of obtaining gold.

The MS reveals that a kind of oil exudes from the bulbous root of the lotus, all around it within a radius of ten cubits. Oily water is exuded and a venomous snake lives under it. To test the properties of the bulb, a needle is to be pierced into it which it dissolves at once. Having procured this bulb, it should be rubbed with mercury in a mortar three times and the oil should be added which is to be heated in a crucible. Then it should be lighted with the embers of bamboo and be heated. Immediately the mercury is killed and acquires the property of converting one hundred thousand times its own weight of the base metal into gold. (Chapter 1, lines 12-19).

The next chapter discusses a substance - raktavījakāṭu which was claimed to have the effect of enhancing prosperity. After purifying copper with care, the juice of raktavījakaṭu should be thrown into copper. The copper will surely turn into Gāngeya gold. The MS then mentions that putting .....(?) in water , the juice should be thrown into it (?) which will turn silver into the colour of kunda flower and taking half a rattika of that silver and throwing it into any metal, it will brighten up, just like gold. With these ends the third chapter in Svarṇatantra.

Another chapter has been named as Kaṭutumbi, which has been interpreted as bittergourd, But one is not very certain about it. In this chapter Lord Śiva advises Paraśurāma that one requires to go to the forest of Kaṭutumbī and after spells and prayers, if bitter seeds are seen, such a one should be cut with care with needles of copper and zinc alloy (?) and in the month of Kārtika, the needle must be inserted inside the fruit . It must be done with proper attention so that the seeds are not pierced or it would be destroyed. Until the month of Māgha, the fruits must be kept in close vigilance and after a month the needles must be extracted. Then the needles should be set on fire, according to the text, on embers of forest stone (?) in an Similarly, in Chapter 1, lines 21-24, it is mentioned: "Saptadhā pratyahaṁrāma tevam viśaddinam dhruvam / ..../Vanāe kāṁsya yadā dadyā tada roupyam bhavet suta".

It points out that pure orpiment is to be rubbed with this oil for twenty days and the former is killed thereby and loses its volatility. The tāla should be thrown into eight molten metals, which being treated with this prepared orpiment, acquires the power of transmutation. When the above oil is thrown into molten copper, it is turned into gold of yellow lustre.

Another process of transmutation has been given in the MS for tin and bell metals as well, using similar process of throwing the so-called oil into the molten metals, but instead of turning gold , they will turn silver.(Chapter 1, line 24)..

In Chapter 1, line 26-28, the author mentions "Chāyāyām khalaṇam kāryamekaviṁśamdinam suta/ louham patre dadhyat pāradasya rasasaṁyuta/...... Tadhatra chullikāyām sthāpayet yatnena suta".

The lines have been deciphered in a way that the expert should take the pārada (mercury) inside and rub it in a mortar for twenty days in the shade.The mercury should then be put in an iron machine (?) both in equal quantities. Then the mudrā named ghôrā should be put in turn which would be carefully placed in the oven.

In the last few lines (29-35) of Chapter1, the entire part is not deciphered yet, but few terminologies like 'araṇyāgni', or forest-fire, 'śabdam' or sound could be easy understandable. The Chapter ends with the concluding lines about wish fulfillment of the wish maker who can turn his property into a hundred fold. Śiva then asks Paraśurāma: "What else do you wish to hear?". With these words ends the first chapter on oil bulb (Taila Kanda) in Svarṇatantra.

As already mentioned there are several chapters in Svarṇatantra, the second chapter has been named as 'Kaṭukusmāṇḍa Kalpa.' It is also in a dialogue form between Lord Śiva and Paraśurāma. Lines 1-4 of the MS states that if the juice of kaṭukuṣmānda is taken and put in tin, silver is created. And in the same way if it is put into copper and iron, it turns gold; the juice should be rubbed with seven metals again and again, making it hundred times powerful. Here ends the second chapter on Svarṇataṇtra.

The third chapter of the MS has been named as 'Raktavījakaṭu' as understandable from it. In this chapter lines1-2, mentions that the juice of should be placed in an raktavijakaṭu, earthen dish. The needles should be placed in the juice and thus will become gold.Here ends the fourth chapter.

Chapter five has been named as 'Siddhatumbi' where tin becomes gold and Chapter six as 'Śvetagokṣura kalpa', where there is special mention of gokṣuraja juice which when treated with tin becomes gold.

Chapter seven of the text is names as 'Śvetaeraṇḍa', where it is mentioned that taking the roots of the śvetaraṇḍa when the sun is in the Puṣya constellation, rubbing its oil with camphor and anointing the eyes with it, will show the seven pātālas (?).

Chapter eight has been named as 'Kākaṛi' where the kākari or kāka fruit is to be plucked when ripe and its juice must be mixed with mercury firmly in a mortar. If it is rubbed for a day, the mercury will harden and for the next twenty days it should be mixed with the juice . By mixing this juice guṭiṣaṣṭhimukha is obtained. Mercury is to be mixed with the juice of the five parts (?) which is placed in a crucible and again juice is put into it. For one night the juice is to be put there. This kills the mercury and taking a rattika of the mercury, if one feeds on it with care, the person lives for ever, without any wrinkles, his hair does not turn white, and he becomes handsome. The juice then should be placed in haritāla and rubbed in a mortar for eight nights, whereupon it becomes smokeless. The juice of that leaf should be thrown in molten tin and the matter that is created, is the colour of kunda flower and if the juice of that fruit is thrown in molten copper, it turns gold.

Chapter nine is named as 'Siddhasvarṇasya Kalpa' which mentions obtaining of pure gold from the wish-yielding tree vôgari (whether this is kalpataru tree is not known) probably found in Karnataka.

Five names of gold presumably – tālakam in east, swarga in west have been interpreted and the others could not be deciphered. Taru(?) is interpreted as having flowers like the kārpāsa (?) . The flower has been mentioned in the MS as supernatural and that the branches of the tree may be broken off and replanted. The tree will grow again fully to its appreciation and with the juice of this flower, mercury is killed. Then it is to be rubbed with this juice for three nights and heat it.

However the mercury is again supposed to be rubbed with the juice of its leaf for eight nights and is then placed in a sealed earthen pot and that tāla (?) should be killed and put in a pot called 'gajā'. Taking the juice of that fruit, it is to be thrown in molten copper which will become pure gold and tin assumes the colour of kunda flower. Thus, the juice mixed with any other metal takes on its quality hundredfold, gold becomes gold, silver becomes silver.

The tenth chapter does not have a clear name in the MS. It could probably be Dagdharohā Kalpa .It mentions that the wood of some (?) plant is to be taken which burn itself into embers which again turns into a tree. That tree (?) should be taken and five parts of embers, the mercury should be placed in a vessel for twenty-one days and then it is killed. Taking that, it should be thrown in any metal, immediately the metals change and placing the wood (?) in a crucible, copper must be thrown into it, which will certainly turn gold. But silver will remain silver.

Here we come to an end of the MS Svarnatantra. The last chapter ends in an abrupt way, which indicates, as already mentioned earlier, that it is an incomplete text. Moreover a proper dating could not be ascribed to the text. Since alchemy, the forerunner of chemistry has emerged in the Middle Ages in India, so this text might belong to the period between 9th century to sixteenth century A.D approximately. Leaving the dating part, the question that keeps on striking into our mind is the authenticity, originality and credibility of the MS. In comparison to the present day technology, the means so discussed in the text of obtaining pure gold puts a big question mark.

The first chapter "Taila Kanda" mentions the lengthy proceedings of obtaining the oil exuded by the bulbous root of the lotus seems superficial and under the garb of mythological and religious aspect. No formula or quantity of mercury has been provided to test its credibility. It also mentions of the snake under the water protecting the plant. Now this information appears story-like.

In every chapter there is mentioning of killing of the mercury before consuming the juice, to be handsome or to mix it with other baser metals. Now it is already known to us that mercury is soluble in sulphuric acid upon boiling, readily and completely soluble in nitric acid, and fully insoluble in hydrochloric acid, water and ether. Owing to its heavy weight, around 13.59 and high boiling point 356.6 degree centigrade and melting point -38.85 degree centigrade, it is understandable that the properties so required by the early alchemists to kill the poisonous nature of liquid mercury were indeed very strong. In terms of chemistry mercury when heated produced salts (alkaline) which acted as a reducing agent and perhaps made the transmutation process easier. As already known mercury is used in all electrical apparatus to withstand the heating effect, it acts as anti-fowling in paints and acts as a catalyst and is also used for medicinal or dental preparations. Owing to modern science, about the uses of mercury (though in a limited way) we can possibly understand that mercury is a very highly activated liquid metal. The interesting part is perhaps the ancient Indian alchemists were aware of its properties. Whether mercury really had the power to transmute baser metals into gold or not, remains undercover. Moreover, the ms does not provide the exact quantity required of the metals. Some terminologies are not clear, some words are missed and it creates a problem for the translators to reveal a clear picture of the MS. What has been provided is only an overview of the MS with repetitive mentioning of baser metals being turned into gold and killing of mercury.

While talking about mercury providing salt which allowed metals to dissolve we get some references from P.C.Ray's book "A History of Hindu Chemistry",[5] It mentions that, samkhadravaka (aqua regia) is spoken of as universal solvent. This solvent with mercury is to be placed in a glazed crucible subjected to heat; the mercury thus killed, can convert the eight metals into gold. By partaking of this mercury one becomes immortal, even his urine can convert into gold. Ray in his book "A History of Hindu Chemistry" mentions the different types of gold specified in Rasaśāstra texts, of which three are attributed to mythical and celestial origin and the fourth is called Kṣhaṇija (to get from mines) and the fifth is obtained from transmutation of baser metals. It is mentioned that gold leaf of the weight of one kārṣa is to be smeared with salt and placed between two earthen saucers and heated on a charcoal fire for half an hour, when its true colour will come out.

Ray also mentions Rasaśāstra composition which hold that the best way of killing all the metals is with the ashes of mercury. The next best way is through the agencies of roots, whereas killing of sulphur is at least recommended. If molten gold is taken of the same weight of the ash of mercury and after cooling is powdered and rubbed with lemon juice, cinnabar and then roasted in a covered crucible twelve times, the gold thus acquires the colour of saffron.

What happens chemically during the process of transmutation, which is a complicated one, cannot be surmised until an experimental verification is attempted. In the ancient period, the alchemists were experts in handling the conversion process. But with it was attached the mythod-religious aspect, the divine male-female symbolism (Śiva and Pārvati), the Bhairava form of Śiva as the creative emblem and its association with the cinnabar (mercuric sulphide) which acted as a fear factor for the ordinary men and prevented commoners to be directly involved in this process.[6]

Suvarnatantra has been divided into ten chapters where each chapter gives its own specialization of the methods of transmutation. Some of the experiments so deciphered from the text have been given in the previous pages but since most of the slokas remains undecipherable, it has not been possible to provide an appropriate justification to the text.

Had this text been cultivated in its fullest form, it would have been easier for the general mass for understanding the theories so given here. No doubt the theories must be authentic in their own way, but due to our lack of proper knowledge and understanding it was not justly appreciated.

It can only be suggested that the experts on pharmacy and chemistry and Ayurvedists sit together on a joint venture, then perhaps the chemical properties of the text can be easily reached and we hope that the text provides us with a valuable information regarding transmutation. No matter, it is understandable from the MS, that it carries weight though put under the garb of religion. But unless it is tested it would only remain a mystery to us. The alchemists's process of transmuting baser metals into gold and the indirect references to actual chemistry will forever go into the shadows of the past, untouched because of its difficult script. At the end it remains a question why was there such a gold rush? Whether this process was used by the commoners or by the experts only? Or was it a medium of creating fear psychosis among the commoners by the power hungry upper class? All this remains a question in the minds of the present day and could only be brought into the limelight by solving the jig-saw puzzle of the difficult script and proper studying of the ancient past.

Bibliography:

1. Khanna: *Theoritical Foundation to Ancient Indian Medicine*, Part -1, New Delhi 1987, 69-75.
2. V.V. Sivarajan & Indira Balachandran: *Āyurvedic Drugs and their plant sources*, New Delhi 1994, 4-5.
3. Mira Roy and B.V. Subbarayappa, edited and Eng. transt. *Rasarnavakalpa, New Delhi, 1993 reprint, Glossary, 'Parada' in, 146, 'rasa' in, 152, 'Suta' in, 161.*
4. Caraka Samhita, Cikitsasthanam, Ch I; Susruta Samihita, Cikitsasthanam, Chs XXVIII - XXX; P.C. Ray, *A History of Hindu Chemistry, Kolkata, 2002, Vol. I : CV and 53.*
5. Ibid.
6. B.V. Subbarayappa: Indian Alchemy: Its Origin and Ramifications, 1999.

7

AYURVEDA IN COLONIAL BENGAL : SURVIVAL AND REVIVAL

Chittabrata Palit

Precolonial History

Ayurveda or the science of life was not the monopoly of the *Brahmins.* It was open to all four castes who could pursue it for religious merit, wealth and pleasure, according to *Charaka Samhita*[1]. The healing arts formed part of secular knowledge and had lay practitioners, the *uisai,* the *ambasthas* and the *chikitsakas.* It was a need-based, utilitarian science but came to be codified in theory arid practice in the texts of Charaka, Susruta and Vagbhata by 5th century A.D. Though hostilities between priest and lay physicians are reported in *Manu Samhita* and other *Brahmasutras, the* thoery of *Brahmanical* spiritualisation and domianation of Ayurveda and *its* consequent decline as a secular science as if it were primarily developed by *non-Brahmins* is unhistorical[2]. There was, in fact, considerable accommodation of secular knowledge like Ayurveda within the sacred texts and it as developed by both *Brahmin* and *non-Brahmin* scholars from *Atreya* to *Vagbhata.* The conflict was more between practitioners of medicine and of surgery as *Brahmins* concentrated more on the former and the non-*Brahmins* on the latter. Ayurveda was treated as an *Upaveda* and its absorption in cosmology was a common trend prevailing over medicine in preindustrial Europe, There was no golden past from which there was a steep decline due to Greek-Scythian or Muhammedan invasions as many revivalists tend to uphold. Considering worldwide state of the art, Ayurveda would compare favourably with Egyptian, Greek and Chinese medicine. But it had certain inherent weakness. Its physical theories of five elements *(Pañchabhutas),* three humors *(Tridosha)* and seven substances (Saptadhatus) cannot be rationally reconciled to each other. Its anatomy was incomplete. In *Caraka* and *Susruta,* properties of head and heart are not properly delineated as they were not subjected to dissection. There was no clear conception whether blood was a humor or a substance. There was no knowledge of the viscera. *Susruta* is better on bones, nerve-junctures, entrails and ducts. All diseases were thought to be due to imbalance of the humors and restoration of their equilibrium was thought to be the cure [3]. There is no place for germ theory or genetic decay of organs in Ayurveda. There is over reliance on texts or *Aptavakyas* and neglect of experimental verification. All natural sciences had an evolution based on experience. Even perception of truth is relative and not immutable. Ayurveda became stagnant because of its textual orthodoxy uninformed by case-histories. In the days of difficult transport and communication, knowledge could not become public and universal. There were no printed books and manuscripts were hoarded as secret knowledge and source of wealth. A few fortunate possessors of Ayurvedic texts would set up their *gurukuls* which kept them confidential *Gurukuls* and later *Tols* depended on a variety of versions of the *Brihadtroyi, i.e., Charaka, Susruta* and *Vagbhata,* rarely induced secrecy. Its commercial value was duly exploited. The *kaviraj* or *vaidya* prepared his own medicine. As a practitioner, it was the secret of his material success. The materia medica was not disclosed or standardised. It remained crude and improvised. In Ayurveda, each individual was considered unique and the treatment was person specific. It was unable to cope with epidemics and unknown diseases caused by bacteria. Common factors and therapies were not developed for general benefit[4]. These inherent defects are glossed over by the revivalists and the blame for decline of Ayurveda is solely put on Muhammedan and British patronage of their Yunani and western medicines. The Muslim, especially, the Mughal rulers were not at all inimical to Ayurveda. Though they brought the Unani system of medicine with them, they also encouraged Ayurveda as a cure. Harun-al-Rashid is known to have welcomed a vaidya to his court at Baghdad for treatment. As Basham observes; 'The practitioners of the two systems seem to have collaborated because each had much to learn from the other and whatever the *ulama* and the *Brahmans* might say, we have no record of animosity between Hindus and Muslims in the field of medicine'[5]. Poonam Bala has given the whole list of integrated medical works and institutions partronised by the Mughals since Babur[9a.b.c]. Ayurvedists also absorbed considerable knowledge from Unani medicine. Blood as an additional humor or substance, sphygmology or pulse lore, use of mercury and opium in specific cases were concepts directly derived from the Unani system[7]. There is, therefore, little basis for the revivalist propaganda that Ayurveda declined due to Muhammedan rule. In fact, the integrated approach made it a living science. Before concluding this section, it can be said that though in Europe, a classical ideal was used to oppose medieval scholasticism during renaissance, scientific knowledge was demythologised with the scientific revolutions in the following centuries and the literal authority of the classical age was challenged. In India, the revivalists clung to the literal texts of ancient times despite progress of medical science since then. Even the integrated approach prevalent in precolonial India was given up.

Colonial Status

From Warren Hastings to William Bentinck, colonial rule was precarious not only due to traditional resistance it had to smother and pacify through coercion and conciliation but also due to the rigours of the tropical climate and diseases which threatened the physical existence of the ruling class. They were avid for all kinds of information about the land and its people-its flora and fauna, mineral resources, language and literature, law and administration, science, technology and medicine, religion, manners and customs. A spirit of paternalism prevailed during this period of collection and compilation of information in order to classify and control it for effective rule. The Asiatic Society (1984), the Botanical Gardens (1987), the Serampore Mission (1799), the Fort William College (1802) and the Agrihorticultural Society (1820) were the fora through which information was gathered. William Jones, the founder of the Asiatic Society was the first to write perceptively on indigenous medicine in his 'Botanical Observations on Select Indian Plants' between 1790-1800. In 1813, the Court of Directors of the East India Company recommended to its government in India the study of Indian tracts on medicine, 'the knowledge of which might prove desirable to the European practitioners'[8]. This was followed by Whitelaw Ainslie's Materia Medica of Hindoostan. In 1822, the Native Medical Institution (NMI) was established and in 1826, parallel instructions in Ayurveda and Unani medicine was started in Sanskrit College and Calcutta Madrasa along with teaching of western medicine through translated western texts. In 1833, more teachers were appointed to teach *Caraka, Susruta* and *Vagbhata* in these institutions. Both NMI and Sanskrit College continued this practice till 1835. Pandit Madhusudan Gupta began his career as an Ayurvedic teacher at Sanskrit College. Students qualifying from these institutions were absorbed as native doctors in civil and military establishments. This policy of accommodation was, however, given up in 1835 after the so called victory of the Anglicists over the Orientalists but really after the consolidation of British rule in Bengal had given the authorities the confidence to override the indigenous system and introduce western medicine. The NMI and the departments of indigenous medicine at Sanskrit College and Madrasa were abolished by Government order of 28 January 1835.

Calcutta Medical College as the pioneer of western medicine took their place with English as the medium of instruction. Madhusudan Gupta was retained on the staff of the CMC as the sole survivor[9a.b]. Madhusudan Gupta led the dissection of the corpse at the CMC against. caste taboo and *Shastric* injunctions. He became the hero and harbinger of western medicine and was presented a self-portrait with the words 'the first Hindu anatomist of British India' written into it by Dr. Goodeve and Bethune. But from the Ayurvedist's point of view, it was a case of surrendered identity by the scion of an Ayurvedist family of repute. The cannonfire salute of fifty rounds from the Fort William simultaneously sounded the death-knell of Ayurveda. By adjuring Ayurveda, Madhusudan was guilty of national betrayal. He qualified as a sub-assistant surgeon for the Health Service and though versatile in both indigenous and western medicine, ended his career carrying a salary of Rs. 200 per month[10a.b]. Though supersession was a matter of policy, appropriation of indigenous medicine in British Pharmacopoeia continued unabated as they were cheaper and easily accessible tropical medicines unknown to the authorities. Thus Brooke O' Shaughnessy compiled Bengal Pharmacopoeia in 1837 dealing exclusively with the properties and uses of the medicinal plants in Bengal. A medical laboratory was established in Calcutta to process and prepare drugs from them. The indigenous materia medica was tapped and authorities consulted in selecting and standardising such drugs for test in hospitals and charitable dispensaries all over Bengal. Several such drugs like *Canriabis indica* were added to the British Pharmacopoeia. During 1839-40 cholera epidemic, country medicines such as *kaladana, but kelija* and drugs composed of opium and calomel were extensively used following their success at Chittagong dispensary[11]. In 1868, the Government published the

Pharmacopoeia of India. The eventual purpose;of this scientific activity was to appropriate many indigenous into British Pharmacopoeia[12]. It was the government policy to insist on low-cost indigenous drugs against the wishes of allopathic practitioners who wanted western medicine imported from England at an enormous cost. The Medical Department in 1866 ordered that indigenous drugs should be used more generally and 'the ones available in a crude and uncouth form be given laboratory treatment before administration' and supplied to all government dispensaries in the presidency[13]. Along with this appropriation of drugs, the rural kaviraja and hakeems were also systematically absorbed within the Health Service. In an official report of 1870, the following table of doctor : people ratio under the Health Service was given for some districts of Bengal:

On an average, 1 doctor of the above group was available fpr every 2000 people for all Bengal. This was hopelessly inadequate. Nor could poor people in the countryside afford costly European drugs like quinine. Indigenous herbal medicines were used by allopathic doctors. The colonial government was unwilling to provide the required number of staff trained in western medicine for rural Bengal. The skeletal Health Service only served the government establishments in the urban areas. So there was an effort to affiliate the *kaviraja* and *hakeems* of the mofussil in the Health Service and encourage them to adopt western system while they practised indigenous medicine. This was the least expensive way of introducing European medicine in rural area. During cholera and malaria epidemics, this was the subordinate paramedical force invariably used[14a]. But still the staff was inadequate to tackle the emergency and the rural people had to depend on their village *Kavirajas* and *dais.* We get a. glimpse of the situation in Hooghly in the 1870s from the memoir of Carstairs:

Bengal's one Sanitary Commissioner used to go about making suggestions which were seldom attended to save near cantonments. Serampore's one Government Doctor fully occupied with the mills, hospitals, patients and town work he had to attend to, seldom saw the villages, save on one of his rare and hasty visits of inspections to a country dispensary or when sent for by some rich invalid or extremist. In the towns, we had one or two qualified medical men whose hands were full of private practice. It did not pay such men to settle in the villages where it was so difficult to move about and where the fatalist

Indian grudged their fees. 'Doctors'-ignorant quacks abounded in towns and villages alike. The medical attendents ordinarily employed by the people were the kaviraj-the hereditary physician who, if without a diploma inherited a good stock of experience and the 'Dai' or nurse-midwife.[14b]

Thus, the *kaviraja* and Ayurveda survived despite official patronage of western medicine. But they were increasingly subsumed under its hegemony in the late 19th century. The Government opposed all moves by the *Bhadroloks* to hoist an Ayurvedic institute of education and research. A petition by Ayurvedists for Government grants for such purposes was turned down on the ground that Ayurveda was unscientific. Even private donations to promote the cause were not utilised by the authorities between 1891-93[15].

At the same time, most of the indigenous drugs of tested value were absorbed in the western pharmacopoeia. Western medicine made giant strides towards becoming a highly organised industry by standardisation of drugs through constant experimental verification and refinement, advance in bacteriology, pharmacology, immunology and chemistry and improved techniques of industrial manufacture of drugs reducing cost. Indigenous medicine lagged far behind. The rise of the drug industry in Britain from the late 19th century and its expansion abreast with German pharmaceutical products continued unabated during the interwar period till it reached a turnover of 58 million pounds in sales in Britain by 1946. It had its inevitable impact on colonial India. Due to increased professionalisation, both British and Indian practitioners of western medicine switched over to synthetic drugs. Thus, the dominance of western medicine was virtually complete[16].

Roots of Revival

The domination generated protest in due course. Ayurveda had its roots in rural areas, in *Tol's* and *Gurukul's* left to themselves by the Raj. Allopathy was essentially an urban phenomenon confined to the metropolis and a few other towns. *Kaviraj* or *vaidya* families continued their hereditary profession in the mofussil. Brahmananda Gupta gives a list of eminent *Kaviraj* families running into three generations spearheaded by Gangadhara Ray (1780-1885), Ganga-prasad Sen (1824-1896), Haranchandra Chakrabarty, Sreecharan Sen, Bijoyratna Sen, Gananath Sen, Jaminibhusan Ray, Bijoykali

Bhattacharyya, Bimalananda Tarkatirtha, Prabhakar Chattopadhyay, etc.[17a.b]. Gupta also cites leading schools of traditional Ayurveda in 19th century Bengal:

School	Speciality
East Bengal	
Savar	Preparation of herbal medicine.
Matta	Techniques of examining patients.
Gaila	Diagnosis and prescriptions and preparation of medicines of chemotherapy.
Chandsi	Healing, many kinds of ulcers, fistula and piles.
Chittagong	Treating insanity.
Khandarapara	Treating insanity and construction hut-like temporary hospitals.
West Bengal	
Murshidabad	Reading pulse and diagnosis.
Kumartuli	Medicine (pills of Nilambar do not fail).
Srikhanda	General physicians who sold medicines in the open market and published Ayurvedic texts.[18]

Tol education was not purely theoretical. Students accompanied the *kaviraj* whenever he visited his patients, thus acquiring clinical experience. They also had practical knowledge of collecting raw materials for medicines and preparing drugs under his direction. Gangadhar Ray, the legendary *kaviraj* of the 19th century was born in village Magura in East Bengal and studied in the Tol of *kaviraj* Ramakanta Sen of Vaidya Belghoria. He practised for a while in Calcutta in 1819 but finally moved to Saidabad in Murshidabad where he set up a Tol and trained a number of brilliant students. He acquired abiding fame in therapeutic use of poisons and decoctions, in diagnosis by reading the pulse and in prognosis. He wrote Sanskrit commentaries on 34 texts and composed 41 original works. His commentary on *Caraka* titled *Jalpakalpa* is his lasting contribution to Ayurvedic scholarship. He died in 1885 at the age of 87 holding away over Bengal Presidency even under colonial constraint. While Gangadhara carried out his crusade for Ayurveda in the countryside, Gangaprasad Sen did it in Calcutta, the citadel of western medicine.

Born in Vikrampur, Dhaka in 1824, he learnt Ayurveda from his illustrious father, Nilambar Sen. He began practising in Calcutta under the shadow of Calcutta Medical College. He began preparing and selling medicine as a reply to import of western drugs with a fixed price list and due publicity in the newspapers. As a practitioner, he charged fees which often surpassed those of the British physicians. He published the first Ayurvedic magazine in Bengali. *Ayurveda Sanjivani* as a campaign for the Indian system. He also opened a Tol at home and offered free room and board to his students. He had many eminent patients including Ramakrishna. He died in 1896 as one of the richest men in Calcutta, Gangadhara Ray and Gangaprasad Sen along with their numerous students authored the Ayurvedic renaissance around 1870. It has to be remembered that in the Bengal Census of 1872, only 3769 physicians, surgeons and doctors of western medicine recorded against 23,700 vaids and hakeems. Bijoyratna Sen, a disciple of Gangaprasad Sen translated the *Astangahridaya* of *Vagbhata,* one of the *bridhatroyis* (old texts) of Ayurveda into Bengali and also published the original Sanskrit text with his emendations. He had many Europeans as his patients and his accomplishments were recognised by the Government of India by conferring on him the honorary title of *Mahamohopadhyay.* He had a good command of English and Allopathy. He sought to integrate the two systems by utilising allopathic medicines as preparations of some of his special medicines. He inspired his student, Jaminibhusan Ray to set up an Ayurvedic college where all eight branches of Ayurveda would be taught. Jaminibhusan was also a scholar of both systems. A man of the 20th century, he sought to rejuvenate Ayurveda against heavy odds. He revived all eight branches of Ayurveda by publishing suitable texts. He introduced *misra-Ayurveda* or integrated medical course in his college by adopting 65% Allopathy and 35% Ayurveda in the mixed course. This was done out of conviction and necessity to get Government grants. Kaviraj Gananath Sen, a coadjutor of Jaminibhusan in founding the Astanga Ayurvedic College was another exponent of both systems. He tried the same integration by writing a Sanskrit treatise on western anatomy titled *'Pratyaksha Shariram'* for students of Ayurveda. He was criticised by the purists or *Shuddhists* like Haranchandra Chakrabarty for considering Susruta inadequate in anatomy[19a1].

Revivalist Strategies

What Jaminibhusan and Gananath tried was one of the ways of revitalising Ayurveda. But Purists attacked it for being neither here nor there. Those who passed the integrated course with a few papers on each system did not learn either Ayurveda or Allopathy fully. They failed to earn people's esteem as reliable doctors. What the purists upheld was the infalliability of the ancient Ayurvedic texts of *Caraka, Susruta* and *Vagbhata* which needed painstaking revision in the light of modern science. As has been pointed out at the outset its anatomy, humoral theory of disease, crude drugs and their toxicity had all to be updated and standardised. When the colonial government tightened up medical education in favour of western medicine by derecognition of practitioners of integrated medicine, stoppage of grants-in-aid and refusal to recruit Ayurvedic graduates on par with the medical graduate in the Health Service and pushed synthetic western medicine through government network of hospitals and dispensaries, the indigenous camp was divided between the integrationists and purists. Public opinion was already regimented by the hegemonic control of British and Indian practitioners of western medicine. It was a fact that the Ayurvedic colleges failed to attract the best students to their discipline and got the failed candidates of the other stream who could not claim the same status with the allopathic brotherhood in terms of pay and position. It was futile to combine both streams by learning each separately for several years. The government disallowed a condensed allopathic course for Ayurvedic students after their graduation in the main stream. The revivalists replied to these predicaments in several ways. They sought legitimacy by political means. They formed a pressure group in the Indian National Congress which passed numerous resolutions in the early decades of the 20th century for government patronage and protection of Ayurveda. The All India Ayurvedic Congress was founded in 1907 to mobilise popular support and pressurise the government. The struggle for Ayurveda came to be identified as freedom struggle[20a13]. Jaminibhusan's Astanga Ayurvedic College and Hospitals was founded in 1916. In 1921, *Gaudiya-Sarva Vidyayatana,* a national university was established of which *Vaidya Sastra Pltha* was an integral part teaching pure Ayurveda. Kaviraj Shyamdas Vachaspati, the founder-principal received a donation of Rs. 6000 from Tilak Swaraj Fund. It continues even today. The Govindasundari Ayurvedic College was founded in 1922 by Kaviraj Ramchandra Mullick and patronised by Manindrachandra Nandy, Maharaja of Kashimbazar. It followed integrated medicine. The Viswanath Ayurveda Mahavidyalaya also founded in 1922 by Gananath Sen was another similar institution studying Ayurveda and Allopathy side by side[21]. The parallel education programme was vigorously maintained from private resources. With Montford Reforms of 1919 and the Government formed by Indian leaders Ayurvedic medicine got some official patronage. State Faculties of Ayurvedic Medicine were formed to promote it. But all government committees to review the state of Ayurvedic education were dominated by allopathic practitioners who were generally cold towards it in recommending official support of any kind and remained undecided in commitment between integrated and pure streams[22]. The only strategy that succeeded was the manufacture of Ayurvedic drugs on a commercial scale by a few entrepreneurial Ayurvedists and chemists. Gupta writes; 'Gangadhara Ray is said to have laughed at practitioners who prepared medicines before hand cabling them *Badial,* possessors of pills ready for common use. But the large scale of production of medicine became necessary as the popularity of Ayurveda grew and small scale preparations could not keep pace with the demand.'[23]. Chandrakishore Sen, a *kaviraj* of the Srikhanda School was the pioneer in the field of commercial manufacture of Ayurvedic drugs. He began it in 1878 at Kalighat on a small scale. Encouraged by success, he shifted to Kolutola to set up his factory for large scale production. C.K. Sen and Co. became a major concern and played a pivotal role in the development of Ayurveda. It also published inexpensive books on Ayurveda to propagate knowledge. A major swadeshi enterprise of the 20th century was the Ayurveda Mahamandal Co. Ltd. which was launched on 21 July 1919 at 19, Grey Street, Calcutta, with an authorised capital of Rs. 50,000. It had the active backing of *zamindars,* bankers and merchants. The managing agency was entrusted to the hands of Kaviraj Surendranath Dasgupta and Jogendrachandra Sastri. Its *Viswanath Taila,* a painkiller and *Sonitamrita,* a blood-purifier were prepared through indigenous methods. In 1914, Gananath Sen, the leading Ayurvedist and the spearhead of Ayurvedic movement in India as the secretary of Ayurveda Sabha and President of the Allahabad Session of the All India Ayurvedic Congress in 1911, launched his Kalpataru Ayurvedic Works, capable of producing drugs on a mass scale in 1914. He purchased a huge disintegrator driven by electricity which manufactured medicines on a large scale and shaped them into tablets. *Chavanprash* and *Makaradhwaja* were some of its best selling products at a cheap rate. But the crowning glory came with the establishment of Sakti and Sadhna Ausadhalayas, both having headquarters at Dhaka which exist even today. Sakti Ausadhalaya was established in 1901 by Mathuramohan Chakrabarty, a chemistry teacher of a high school, out of his salary savings. It had branches at Banaras, Calcutta and Rangpur and produced drugs on a mass scale from both vegetables and minerals. A team of *Kavirajs* were employed for the purpose. *Chavanprash*, *Makaradhwaj* and *Saribadi Salsa*, were its well known products. Jogeshchandra Ghosh, the founder of Sadhana Ausadhalaya in 1914 was a lecturer in chemistry at Bhagalpur College and a student of Sir P.C. Ray. Its *Mritasanjivani Sudha* and *Mahadrakshanshta* became popular recuperative tonics. It has remained in business for the last 77 years and has branches all over India and Bangladesh. Kaviraj Naresh Ghosh, son of Jogeshchandra who runs the . business is also a major Ayurvedist missionary in his own right. He has presided over many provincial Ayurvedic conferences and pointed out the efficacy of cheap Ayurvedic treatment and medicine for poor masses of India who cannot afford costly allopathic medicine[24].

Postcolonial Prospect

In the freedom struggle in the field of medicine, Ayurveda had successfully countered the 'para medical subordination to the cosmopolitan medical profession' by professionalisation and institutionalisation, politicisation for legitimacy and technologically advanced manufacture of mass medicines. It was a case of modernity of tradition. As Brass writes, 'the penetration of modern medicine into the country side has been so slow that there is no real prospect of providing relief to the rural areas of India.........in the generations to come'[25]. It is in this gap that professionalised Ayurveda has come to stay. But it should not mean that the revivalist movement should score a point by asserting that all modern medical developments were anticipated in ancient India. The demand to declare Ayurveda as the national system of medicine and the cry of quit India against western medicine is sheer chauvinism. One may not superscribe to Brass's view that 'dual modernisation in India is a wasteful process' and an integrative approach should be taken to combine the best elements of both systems[26]. This would result in the assimilation of the one by the other as happened in the colonial past. The government and the vocal public are already biased in favour of western medicine. Leslie more perceptively writes: 'we should not assume as laymen, and physicians in the United States usually do, that the ideal of a uniform medical system controlled by physicians of cosmopolitan medicine is intrinsically superior to other ideals and should be the goal of all societies. The pluralistic structure of the Indian medical system might best develop toward goals that would enhance the advantages of pluralism while correcting its disadvantages'[27].

While its anatomy and humoral theory of disease are inadequate in the light of modern science, Ayurveda still retains its efficacy in chronic elemental diseases; its treatment of the patient rather than the impersonal disease so relevant today in psychosomatic syndromes; its prognosis and diagnosis and pulse lore are areas deserving greater attention and improvement through logistic support of modern science. Though it is not true that all Ayurvedic drugs are non-toxic (crude, narcotic and metallic drugs do have high toxicity needing control), they are by and large more natural absorbents in the body with little or no side-effects. Ayurveda also has a socio-cultural context in which family involvement takes precedence over quarantine of the patient. Most of all, its range of indigenous drugs are all tropical and of bewildering variety. They are more suitable for tropical diseases, easily and heaply available for rural masses and present an inexhaustible resource for human cure. Pitted against this profile of Ayurveda, all allopathic drugs as active chemicals are toxic to various degrees with side-effects more severe than the disease itself.

Most of them being synthetic products can be rejected by pathogens by being resistant to them. The diagnostic assessment is quantitative and not qualitative. Western pharmacopoeia become cosmopolitan by appropriating much of Ayurveda by superior technology and standardisation. The medicinal properties of *Chalmugra* oil and *Bel* or *wooden apple* as cure for leprosy and dysentery have already become common factors in both systems. Such possibilities are immense, given the logistic support of modern science and can tackle many diseases declared incurable in allopathy. This is the fourth and final option for free India. Brass while deploring Ayurvedic revivalist chauvinism and preaching integration of Ayurveda within a hegemonic cosmopolitan medicinal system forgets the national self-interest of some of the western countries in swapping Indian indigenous drugs by modern scientific refinement and then patenting them for national benefit and profit. The recent Dunkel proposal on intellectual property rights is an eye-opener for all integrationists. Leslie on a sober note concludes, if a wizard of modernization decided that 'traditional medicine was an impediment to progress and abolished tomorrow the whole infrastructure of professionalised Ayurvedic and Yunani practices, he would create a medical catastrophe.[28]

President Radhakrishnan in his foreword to Kutumbiah's book, the *Ancient Indian Medicine* says: 'The system of medicine will have to keep pace with the developments of time. Our systems suffered because they were not able to reckon with the progress made.' Ayurveda has to live upto this challenge and must be updated and upgraded by modern science and technology without having to sacrifice its world of experience. There is a need to scientifically explore the correlation of ancient insights and modern discoveries beyond the narrow trajectory of purity pollution[29].

REFERENCES

1. Kutumbiah, P.: Ancient Indian Medicine, Madras 1962: Introduction, C.S, 130:24.
2. Chattopadhyay, D.P.: Science and Society in Ancient India, Calcutta 1977:112,213, 273.
3. *Op.cit.*, Kutumbiah 1962 : 32.
4. Leslie, Charles ed.: Asian Medical Systems: A Comparative Study, London, 1976 "The Ambiguities of Medical Revivalism in Modern India in Leslie ed. 1976; 356-57.
5. Basham, A.L.: 'Practice of Medicine in Ancient India' in Leslie, C.ed. 1976 below ; 40.

6a. Bala, P : Imperialism and Medicine in Bengal, Delhi, 1991: Appendix A. 14-15.

6b. Also-Keswani, N.H. ed.: The Science of Medicine and Physiological Concepts in Ancient and Medieval India, New Delhi, 1974.

6c. Rashid, A: Society and Culture in Medieval India, Calcutta, 1969.

7. *Op.cit.,* Leslie 1976 : 356-57.
8. Op.cit., Bala 1991:41.

9a. *Ibid.,* Bala 1991: 47.

9b. Ukil, A.ed.: Century Volume of the Medical College, Bengal 1835-1934, Calcutta 1935.

10a. Palit, C: New Viewpoints on Nineteenth Century Bengal, Calcutta 1980: 68-69.

10b. Chattopadhyay, P.: Ayurveder itihas (History of Ayurveda) in Bengali, Cal-1963:162-63.

11. *Op.cit.,* Govt. Charitable Dispensaries 1840-42 in Bala 1991:48-50.

12. Arnold, D.: Imperial Medicine and Indigenous Societies, Mancheater, 1988 'Medical Priorities and Practice in Nineteenth Century British India' South Asian Research Vol. 5 No. 2,1985 :160-83.

13. *Op.cit.,* Bala 1991: 51,

14a. Campbell Brown, J.: Report on the Charitable Dispensaries under the Govt. of Bengal for the year 1870. Calcutta 1871.

14b. Carstairs, R.: The Little World of an Indian District Officer, London, 1912:154-55.

15. Ray, B.B.: Unish Sataker Banglay Vighan Sadhana (Pursuit of Science in 19th Century Bengal) in Bengali, Cal, 1987:97-98.

16. *Op.cit.,* Bala, 1991: 52-57.

17a. Gupta, Brahmananda : 'Indigenous Medicine in Nineteenth and Twentieth Century Bengal' in Leslie, C. ed. 1976: 373-74.

17b. *Op.cit.,* Chattopadhyay, p. 1.963:163-75.

18. Gupta *Ibid.:* 369.

19a. *Ibid.,* Gupta in Leslie ed. 1976 : 371-74.

19b. *Op.cit.,* Chattopadhyay, p. 1983:164-75.

20a. Ibid., Gupta in .Leslie ed, 1976 :375-878.

20b. Ghosh Nareshchandra : Ayurvcd Chikitsa Sastrer Itihas (History of Ayurveda) in Bengali, Cal., 1963 :77.

21. *Ibid.,* Gupta in Leslie ed. 1976; 375-76.

22. Brass, P.R.: 'The Politics of Ayurvedic Education : A case study of revivalism and modernization in India' in Rudolph and Rudolph eds. Education and politics in India, Chicago, 1972 : 344-352.

23. *Op.cit.,* Gupta in Leslie ed.: 374-375.

24. Bhattacharyya, A: Swadeshi Enterprise in Bengal 1900-1920, Calcutta, 1986 : 58-67.

25. *Op.cit.,* Brass in Rudolph and Rudolph eds. 1972 : 351.

26. *Ibid., :* 370-73.

27. Leslie in Lslie ed, 1977 : 357.

28. *Ibid.,* Leslie in Leslie 1977 : 267.

29. Lele, R.D.: Ayurveda and Modern Medicine, Bombay 1986 : Passim.

INDEX